ENDING BIGLY: THE MANY FATES OF DONALD TRUMP

EDITED BY

BILL MARCHANT

Sheridan, WY
Terror House Press
2021

This is a work of fiction. Names, characters, businesses, events, and incidents are the products of the authors' imagination. Any resemblance to actual persons, living or dead, or actual events is purely coincidental.

ISBN 978-1-951897-32-1

EDITORS

Matt Forney (mattforney.com), Bill Marchant (northernreaction.wordpress.com)

LAYOUT AND COVER DESIGN

Matt Lawrence (mattlawrence.net)

TERROR HOUSE PRESS, LLC

terrorhousepress.com

TABLE OF CONTENTS

“...like the Roman...” — John Enoch Powell, MBE

PROLOGUE

I knew a man once. His name, it doesn't matter, but I suppose there's no harm in telling you. His name was Gilbert Florin. He did not live in America for most of his life. He did, however, die in America. Less than a week ago. Yes, the same day Trump died. Gill would have liked that. As the only person in Boston who knew him personally, I was given the unenviable task of clearing out his apartment.

You have to understand: Gill was a bit of an eccentric. He was a scholar of some repute, but mostly in an infamous sort of way. He had, for example, submitted papers to just about every major journal that focuses on history, politics, philosophy, or literature. Every time he submitted a paper, it would be sent back to him. Sometimes, the journal would reject the paper outright, but mostly they would ask for minor changes. Some more careful language in his conclusions, or a bit less dependence on "the dictates of Providence" in one of his arguments. Nevertheless, there was always something that needed changing. And Gill never would. As soon as he got a rejection from the journal, he would immediately place the paper he wrote, unchanged, on his bookshelf. "Now it's in the universe," he would say. As far as I know, he did this over 100 times. However, some of those papers were quite short. Even the few books he wrote, which were also rejected by a single publisher and placed on his shelf, were less than 300 pages each. Gill would also always use a pen name, even when it was glaringly obvious that it was him writing. And he would always use a different pen name. He once told me he did this because "every work is a new act of creation and deserves a new Creator." I still don't know what that means.

Gill wrote his manuscripts on nearly every subject imaginable at one time or another, but his real passion was American history. I never met anyone else who could name every American Secretary of State in order. And not just the politics of the country, but the geography, the people, the idea of it. The last time I saw Gill alive was about two weeks before he died. He didn't make eye contact with me. He just kept mumbling "What does Trump mean?" and "What will Trump be?" and "How will Trump end?" Knowing Gill for as long as I have, I didn't think anything of it. If he gets an idea in his head, he doesn't think about anything else until he writes it all the way out.

His apartment was almost exactly the same as it had been every other time I had been there. Dozens of bookshelves with hundreds of books. And, of course, right beside his desk was the Manuscript Bookshelf. Besides some dishes in the sink and a couple of papers here and there, the Manuscript Bookshelf was the only thing that was significantly changed from the last time I was there. He had condensed the manuscripts from five shelves down to four, and had stuck a large label on the top shelf that simply said "TRUMP: THE END." On that shelf were documents, dozens of them, arranged in seemingly random order.

I noticed that beside the Manuscript Bookshelf, Gill's typewriter had a piece of paper with typing on it. I knew that Gill had died at his desk. The police didn't think the typing was relevant. I picked up the sheet of paper, "The American Aeneid" by Jim Handler, and started reading.

"America doesn't have a Virgil! America hasn't been connected to the wider myths of civilization! Rome had Aeneas, Britain had Brutus; what does America have? I'll tell you! America doesn't have a Virgil because Virgil comes after Caesar! Trump is America's Caesar; who will be Virgil? Will I be the American Virgil? Which of the myths I've made will become part of the very fabric of America the Empire? HOW WILL TRUMP END?"

Those were the last words Gill wrote. I supposed that the "myths" he was talking about were the documents on the top shelf. They appeared to be in random order, but Gill never did anything arbitrarily. I picked up the first one, "The Rise and Fall of the First Drumpf" by Land Shark, and started reading.

THE RISE AND FALL OF THE FIRST DRUMPF

by Land Shark

A brick-blue sky cracked in thunder as the DON was pacing around his safe room under the Trump Hotel basement, Las Vegas. The carcass of his body double was already lying on the ground next to him, the smell of its burned flesh being tastefully covered under perfume.

"The Yankees are closing in, sir. It's time to go."

"Trump might have died in his Bunker, ashes to floor dust"—Serrano would write years later—"but even if he did (and he did not!), he rose up alive, on the third day, in Neudrumpfenland's secret sub-terrestrial base. And he did so as something else: as a god."

Serrano did not care about the supposed blasphemy that some of his political allies noted as somewhat worrying, for the love he felt for his president was itself the superior principle to his being. Nothing that brought glory to Trump could be blasphemy.

By the time the Yankees broke into the room, it had already been hermetically sealed hours ago. The space was nicely lit, with a few interior items, including a leather chair, a small table supporting a bottle of gin (no glass to be found), and some sort of Buddhist painting on the wall, by all chance found alongside other random objects in the basement.

Something that was left out of the official Yankee report and the newspaper articles was that even though all of the president's other clothes were burned along with his carcass, the MAGA hat was left unscratched on his head.

This naturally presented a very puzzling case, which prompted some tests to be immediately performed on the item, discovering only fingerprints corresponding to those of Donald Trump on its surface.

A few theories were crafted by a think tank consisting of various criminologists and psychoanalysts from Harvard, narrowing down the possibilities to two scenarios only:

Some sort of chemical agent was applied to the MAGA headwear's texture, rendering it temporarily fireproof. The substance used must have had a very short half-life as to be undetectable in the later tests.

It was arranged for the member of the Trump contingent who poured the oil over the corpse and set it aflame to wait until it had finished burning and then place the MAGA hat on its head, possibly as an attempt at a final taunt or a triumph in death. A few classified texts were written and archived concerning the possible psychology behind the act. Some mentioned that the person performing the burning was likely a diehard supporter of Trump's cause and might have performed the "rite" as an idea of his own volition. He had been instructed to wear surgical gloves so as to cover his fingerprints, or decided to do it to protect his own identity.

As neither of the two hypotheses presented any sort of apparent danger, the conclusion was that as far as the public was left unaware of that tiny detail, there was zero risk for the regime.

"I do not believe the DON'S death came through him ingesting a mix of cyanide and morphine."—wrote Serrano with firm fingers—"In the first place, I find zero reason to believe that regular physical substances are able to harm something eternal and above-human. If there truly was a fire, then it was not ignited of flame and matches, but it came from Trump's own inner will. If there truly was a body in that bunker (and there was not!), then it was just a snake shedding its old skin."

Serrano was never prosecuted for his writings, mostly because they were considered whimsical to a degree of true lunacy, and if anything, they just made the leftover Trump supporters seem insane by association.

He enjoyed a lower-middle class life until his death in his 80s, which his few supporters claim he himself predicted.[1*]

As for Donald Trump's body, it was disposed of in the ocean, in

1 Sources say that he had wrongly predicted his death in 15 separate occasions in the years beforehand, rendering the feat somewhat less impressive and more likely to be pure chance.

undisclosed coordinates, just like that of Sheikh Osama. The majority of his loyalists had managed to escape to Russia, where they were stationed in small, dying northern Soviet cities which otherwise served zero economical purpose to the nation.

The cultural figures associated with the DON in the '10's and '20's served various fates. Mikhaila Peterson revealed that she was actually the one to write her late father's infamous books, which was later confirmed by an independent committee of literary experts. She proceeded to isolate herself from public attention, opting for a quiet life with her new husband, Igor, in an undisclosed location. Previous enemies Ben Shapiro and Professor Richard Spencer finally could embrace each other as brothers, their enemy finally defeated. They would later collaborate in Deleuzo-Guattarian fashion, producing their masterpiece *Resisting from Two Sides,* today considered one of the 21st century's finest works.

As history carried on, Trump remained as but a footnote, and after the death of Serrano, only state historians concerned themselves with studying that dark epoch.

"A last MAGA march remains to pass. A final MAGA march will come from the moon," screamed Pence in his jail cell months after the DON'S demise.

He, too, had lost his mind, as many others had done in the era of Trump. But it was all finally over. Justice had triumphed in the land of the Yankees.

As thunders echoed in the canyon, something ancient was waking under the ice of Antarctica.

DONALD TRUMP: A WHOLESOME DR. MABUSE

by Elias Kingston

I want Donald Trump to be Caesar. I want him to be Napoleon. I would love to see the day when he, the descendant of King Christian I of Denmark, Norway, and Sweden, is crowned as Emperor Donald I in a gold-bedecked ballroom in Washington, D.C. However, I'm not sure any of that will happen. Like Victor Davis Hanson in his book *The Case for Trump,* I see in Trump the figure of the tragic hero. He may have his de Gaulle moment where he tears down the cultural and Big Tech barricades and saves the Republic, but many signs point to a punished and martyred hero who will only be revered by all American citizens once the true horror of neoliberal totalitarianism is revealed.

This is no "blackpill," friends. I think that Trump will never die in any real sense. He will be a wholesome Dr. Mabuse who plagues the minds of the left and will continue to serve as an inspiration to the real right throughout the West.

First penned by author Nobert Jacques in *Dr. Mabuse, der Spieler* (1921), Dr. Mabuse was, for a time, the German equivalent of France's Fantomas and Britain's Professor Moriarty. An arch-criminal with grand designs to be the ruler of a tropical kingdom, Dr. Mabuse, in Jacques's novel, is a lustful and ambitious criminal who embodies the frenzied and feverish capitalism of the newly democratized German nation. This is not the Dr. Mabuse I have in mind. My Mabuse, and the Trumpian Mabuse, is the one that is found in Fritz Lang's 1933 film, *The Testament of Dr. Mabuse.* An obvious excoriation of Adolf Hitler and the Nazi Party, Lang's

Dr. Mabuse is a criminal genius whose insane scribblings literally possess Dr. Kramm (played by Theodor Loos). Dr. Mabuse's ideology of terrorism is called the "Empire of Crime." Dr. Mabuse's theory of horror includes frightening the general population with "unfathomable and seemingly senseless crimes" in order to shake all of us to our depths. This is the left's conjuration of Donald Trump: the spirit of autocracy packed in a badly-tanned skinsuit. He's "literally Hitler," after all. And like Dr. Mabuse, his attacks on "our democracy" are so profoundly destabilizing that they require extreme measures in order to stop the crime from spreading. This means oppression across the board; online, at work, and in your own mind.

To those of us on the real right, Trump is still Dr. Mabuse, but we take different lessons. Dr. Mabuse's criminal networks in Weimar Germany exposed the many vulnerabilities of that desiccated republic, and likewise, the MAGA movement has served to enlighten millions of normies about the prevalence of naked power. The elite rules because they exert the most power in multifaceted ways. Antifa and Black Lives Matter are the street thugs of the establishment, while the courts and bureaucracy serve neoliberal totalitarianism rather than the law. And, as Christopher Caldwell shows in *The Age of Entitlement,* the Constitution and anachronistic ideals of liberty are intentionally suppressed under the ever-expanding mandate of civil rights. Without Trump, most Americans would continue to believe the lies about fairness and the supremacy of law and blind justice.

President Trump, the great tribune of Foundational America, has been subverted at all turns by the D.C. Establishment, and he continues to be betrayed by the very institutions he sought to save, like the Supreme Court. This is definite "end of the republic" energy, and Trump should be celebrated for waking up millions to the illegitimacy of mass democracy and all its adherents. Trump, like Stilicho, sought to preserve a dying empire for a few more years. However, he has learned to embrace the anarchy of Dr. Mabuse and go fully into exposing the Empire of Crime. The only difference is that he is the victim of the criminal empire, while the "adults in the room" and those who blather about "decency" are the true and truly degenerate criminals. This is what makes him wholesome, as he exposes and suffers from criminal conspiracies rather than perpetuate them.

The final Mabuse-like element to Trump is that he, like Dr. Mabuse, will never truly die. To the left, Trump will continue to haunt their nightmares as the purveyor of incipient fascism, even if they make the tactical mistake of putting Trump on trial and/or executing him. Doing so would make Trump, who is already a martyr in so many ways, something worth killing and dying for. A Trump execution or imprisonment would certainly create a Bastille moment, except it would be the technocratic Jacobins suffering the consequences rather than the Royalists. For the real right, Trump will serve the same function as the faceless and formless Dr. Mabuse, who directs vast networks of criminal insurgents in Weimar Berlin. They do not know it, but the GOP is dead without Trump. Therefore, the American right will be Trumpist for the foreseeable future, and may split like Peronism in Argentina into left-wing and right-wing factions. Rather than take the same marching orders from the GOP, Americans on the right will look to Trump, whether living or dead, for direction. All future policies will be measured by how Trumpian or not they are. This cannot be stopped, thank God.

If for nothing else, Donald Trump has exposed how politics in the United States is mere venality wrapped in a façade of virtue. Democrats and Republicans uphold the Empire of Crime because it makes them and their diseased offspring rich. Trump has already paid many times over for exposing the decrepit inner workings of neoliberal totalitarianism and its multi-party consensus. It is highly likely that, like a hero in a Greek tragedy, he will endure horrific punishment for his selflessness.

So, what will happen to Trump? What happens to him physically is secondary. He may serve another term. He certainly earned it in the face of massive fraud and actual foreign interference. Or he will be thrown out by the Empire of Crime and forced into exile on some newfangled Saint Helena. This is not as important as the fact that Trump, like Dr. Mabuse, will exist as a miasma and figurehead of instability—instability that threatens the Empire of Crime and all its manifold tentacles, and instability that offers eventual salvation for those on the real right.

SIMULACRA AND STIMULATION

by Kashiwagi

I saw the first article back during the trial, I think. It's hard for people to remember these things. Take "fake news," for example. Everyone thinks he came up with that phrase. Maybe sometime in mid-2017 they'll say, if you bother to ask them. They don't remember how he turned the tables with that one. Dozens of op-eds in the week after the election using that line, "fake news," saying that was how he'd done it. Some bogus Facebook link about how the pope had endorsed him. That was what sealed the deal, apparently. It didn't always mean CNN.

But anyway, the article. I wanted to tell you about the article. It was during the trial, I'm pretty sure. Certainly before sentencing. An NYT piece: "A Look Inside USP Leavenworth, President Trump's New Jome." Amid descriptions of its history, the layout of its cells, the day to day affairs of its inmates and so on was an offhand comment about the incidence of violent crime within the prison itself. "Official BOP statistics indicate that over 700 forcible rapes were reported at Leavenworth in 2019, the most recent year for which data is available."

The jokes started on Twitter almost immediately, but it wasn't until a couple days later that the first bluecheck really set things into motion. Some middle-aged sitcom actress posted that she hoped Trump would be "the most popular bottom-bitch in Kansas." It quickly went viral, getting more than 500,000 Likes the evening it went up. Someone, Charlie Kirk maybe, responded by tagging Twitter's CEO. "@jack censors CHINESE DISSIDENTS yet allows MARXIST HATE SPEECH to spread unchecked." Trump Jr. retweeted. It got 15,000 Likes. Jack never responded.

A few self-described "classical liberals" issued muted condemnations of the Tweet. "I denounce the left's vulgarity in much the same way I have Trump's," one *National Review* writer stated. The more common attitude, however, seemed to be one of calculated amusement. A clip of Anderson Cooper struggling to stifle his giggles while discussing the Tweet on *360* made the rounds. One quote-Tweet that simply read "Y'all know we STAN Anderson Cooper" garnered several hundred thousand likes of its own. That Friday, Bill Maher devoted his closing segment to defending the tweet. "It's time for Americans of all stripes to step up and say it: we do hope Donald Trump gets raped in prison." In an appearance on the *Joe Rogan Experience,* Eric Weinstein explained the "Trump Rape Affiliation Paradox" (or TRAP) into which we had fallen. "Those on the left who have decried rape culture for years now ask us to joke about it, if not outright support it," he noted, before launching into an extended anecdote about the new intelligent GPT-3 Go emulator's recursive strategy.

Then the thinkpieces started to emerge. *Vice* ran one titled "Actually, Trump Getting Raped in Prison Would Be Pretty Cool" and some of the other "edgier" outlets put out their own articles expressing similar sentiments. Clickbaity stuff, to be sure. Nothing unexpected. What really got peoples' attention was when the "higher brow" publications started to do the same. I remember one Atlantic headline, "The Cosmic Justice of Donald Trump's Prison Rape," especially well. In it, David Frum wrote that while he would not go so far as to call for Trump to be raped, there would be an undeniable poetry in the man who had so famously described "grabbing women by the pussy" finally experiencing some physical violations of his own.

Bill Kristol Tweeted, "Though I was skeptical at first, I've increasingly come around to the idea that a proud racist and credibly accused rapist like Trump being passed around by disproportionately racial minority prisoners is the appropriate end to such a shameful saga." Shortly afterward, the Lincoln Project's account began replying to Trump's tweets with comments like "Scared of what your cellmate is gonna do to you, sweetie?" and "Oh, honey, just wait till you meet Jamal [nail polish emoji]."

The weekend after the verdict in Trump's trial, *Saturday Night Live* ran a cold open involving a couple of Secret Service guards standing around as prisoners of various different racial and religious minority backgrounds entered and exited a cell where Alec Baldwin, from behind a dark screen, did his pained impression of Trump. "I told you they were rapists. Ahhhhhhhh!" he yelled as a Mexican prisoner took his turn. The biggest laugh line occurred when, much to the guards' surprise, a group of female prisoners showed up carrying red, white, and blue strap-ons. "Looks like orange is the new orange," one said, turning to the camera. The sketch was praised as "genius" in the press, with Andy Borowitz writing in the *New Yorker* that it offered "a visionary new perspective on comedy for the Biden era." The one controversy was over its lack of trans representation, which the writers issued an apology for, promising to "listen and do better" in the future.

It's hard to say exactly when things changed. I'd seen critical replies under articles for a while. Matt Taibbi wrote a Substack post expressing concern at the casual attitude toward rape that respectable opinion had suddenly embraced. "But then, who's really surprised that the same people who covered up the Tara Reade accusations all of a sudden think rape is really funny when it's happening to their enemies?" Alyssa Milano criticized the media for making light of the issue. "The fact that there is rape in prison is a huge problem. A powerful rapist like Trump could easily end up being the one raping other men in prison. No one should be allowed to rape anyone. It's not cute or funny to say this shit."

The "powerful rapist" tweet didn't get much attention, except among certain anonymous right-wing Twitter users who started inserting the phrase "a powerful rapist like Trump" into every headline that used his name and emulating Trump's erstwhile posting style in descriptions of prison life. The format became so popular that a new gimmick account started reimagining Trump's most notable quotes with prison rape as the subject matter.

"We're going to rape so much, you're going to be so sick and tired of raping, you're going to come to me and go 'Please, please, we can't be raped anymore.' You've heard this one. You'll say 'Please, Mr. President, we beg you sir, we don't want to be raped anymore. It's too much!'"

"When they send cellmates, they're not sending their best: they're sending snitches, they're sending pussy-ass bitches."

You get the idea.

The account only lasted eight days before it got banned, but managed to accumulate 73,000 followers in the meantime. In fact, the banning only accelerated the memeing. More and more elaborate descriptions of Trump's proficiency at raping filled every journalist's Twitter replies. It wasn't long before the first articles about "the alt-right's dangerous new meme" started to appear and the SPLC added a page on "Powerful Rapist Trump" to their database of hate.

It died down eventually, as all things do. Biden made another gaffe. He described Kamala as "the first African woman in history." The news focused on equitable distribution of the corona vaccine instead. People started to log off.

Several months after sentencing, the *New York Times* came out with yet another article detailing life inside Leavenworth. This time, though, instead of a general overview, the report was much more narrowly focused on reports from unnamed sources inside the Bureau of Prisons describing how things had changed since Trump's arrival. The atmosphere inside the prison, the report said, had become more divisive. Racial gang violence had seen an uptick, with an alliance between the Mexican Mafia and Aryan Brotherhood making a move on the historically black-owned drug smuggling business.

It was to be the first in an ongoing series of reports, for which the *Times* would eventually win the Pulitzer, detailing the spread of these tendencies from Leavenworth to other prisons across the country. The chaos Trump introduced provided the basis for a widespread review of prison conditions as a whole. Their historical relationship to white supremacy. The sexist assumptions behind disciplinary incarceration. Abuse of trans prisoners was of particular concern, with a record two deaths over the course of 2021, the highest number ever in the federal system.

The latest groundbreaking entry came out just a couple weeks ago. According to anonymous sources at DOJ with contacts among the prison staff, Trump has been the aggressor in multiple sexual assaults since his sentence began. The investigative report details corruption among administrators who have turned a blind eye to both the escalating gang warfare as well as Trump's personal predations. Construction contractors for the newest cellblock, built a decade ago, have been tied to Russian financiers, who various experts have identified as Putin allies.

Since the report's publication, there have been widespread calls for President Biden to fire his attorney general and appoint a special prosecutor to investigate Trump's activities. Protests have wracked the town of Leavenworth as activists show up to make their voices heard. The White House has yet to issue any response, but a CNN crew started broadcasting from outside the gates just this afternoon, and there are reports of people beginning to gather around other federal facilities across the country.

I got a message from an old friend the other day. He'd been big into QAnon stuff, but got banned for posting too much about election fraud. He told me it's all bullshit. That Trump died during his trial. Heart exploded after one too many fish filets. General Flynn and Barron are working on a plan, though. "Just wait and see." Funny story, but I don't put much stock in conspiracy theories.

OLD MAN TRUMP AND THE TOCHKA

by Patrick Kilgore

"He was not to do anything in bad taste, the woman of the inn warned old Eguchi. He was not to put his finger into the mouth of the sleeping girl, or try anything else of that sort." — Yasunari Kawabata, House of the Sleeping Beauties

"At the beginning of the new year, we started to know each other as well as if we lived together awake, for I had discovered a cautious tone of voice that she heard without waking, and she would answer me with the natural language of her body." — Gabriel Garcia Marquez, Memories of My Melancholy Whores

Moscow's first morning chill was much harsher than any he had experienced in Washington D.C. or New York City. Most of the weight he had put on the last few years in the States had shed off him quicker than he thought due to the stress of exile. The Big Macs in Russia weren't as good as America. Old Man Trump slipped into memories of his past life like he did so often now. He was trying to recall the flavor of the best Big Mac he had the pleasure of eating. He even remembered the date: September 3, 2020. There was a rally in Latrobe, Pennsylvania for the upcoming election, and being the fast food aficionado he was, he could never pass an opportunity up for snagging one of these burgers from the location that invented the sandwich back in 1967. Well, someone always snagged it for him when he was around Pittsburgh. Latrobe was only an hour away, so the Big Mac wasn't hard for whoever brought it to him to keep warm. It was there seducing him when he showed up. He chuckled to himself, thinking, *if only the crowd knew I kept them waiting just so I could enjoy the original Big Mac.* He wondered if anyone that was present at that rally, cheering for him in an almost religious jubilee, ever thought about where he was now, if they ever put so much as a single thought into what he was doing day to day in Russia. Before his exile, he was the most talked-about, thought-about, written-about man in the world. Now he is but a faint memory of a dark stain on Usonia's past.

What surprised him the most about his solitude was how quickly he was forgotten. Just another memory hole in the history books that gets one sentence a decade later. And that first decade in Moscow all but killed his ego. The fight with his ego was what he thought would be his eternal struggle. He couldn't tell if it was the bitter cold weather, the absolute loss of creature comforts, the inescapable passage of time and old age, or the harsh Russian attitudes, almost a hatred, he seemed to face when he encountered most strangers.

The first few years, his face was still the one you saw on the TV, and he was treated like a celebrity, like a former world leader, wherever he went. Now only old age is shown on his face. He lost all desire to maintain his last gasps of youth. Away went the Botox and the spray tans. Now all that remains of the greatest entertainer of the modern age is shriveled and unrecognizable. Even his voice has lost that trademark bravado. To say he was a shell of a man would attribute to him a strength that shells seem to possess that he utterly lacked. What would be more accurate is permanent ego death. His gold chic palace and White House residency has been replaced by a small, dank room in brick low-housing in one of the poorest districts in Southern Moscow, Kapotnya. He was moved here from Rublyovka a few years after his exile when it became apparent his influence in American politics was waning.

What he missed most about Rublyovka were the women the Russian government brought to him. They barely provided him enough rubles now to keep him warm and fed. Some uppity bugman at the CIA was able to sniff out all of his hidden offshore, accounts leaving him penniless a few months into his exile. He hated that bastard more than anyone alive and didn't even know his name.

Old Man Trump thought he was going to be able to go along living like he was in his Rublyovka penthouse until he died. He gave up on that idea after his funds were stripped from him and he was unable to supplement the escorts the Kremlin provided him for ones he purchased himself. This nearness to youthful beauty that these escorts brought him helped him hold on to the carefully-crafted image he created for himself.

Old man Trump felt his life closing in on him now. The cold chilled him down to the very marrow of his bones, a new kind of cold he never felt before, and one he was certain was some kind of perverted foreplay on the part of death. A tease for the void that he knew awaited him when he finally passed. What he would give to be around youthful beauty again just one more time. Not in the way that he used to, though. Incontinence came in with the winter chill shortly after the weight loss. But there was a warmth in youth that he craved so. Just to spend one more night in a warm bed with a young, beautiful woman again. Just one more night. He prayed to whoever was listening for this often. Recently, in fact, this was his only prayer. He felt death so close to him now he feared the chance of just one more warm night would hang forever in front of his face like an unripe peach not yet ready to be plucked from the tree. He couldn't taste the peach or feel its nectar run down his jowl with that first bite, but he could pluck it, run his old fingers along the soft down that ran across the orange flesh, smell the familiar sweet juice with a slight hint of acidity to it that hid below the surface, just out of reach.

***

It's been eight long years since his transfer from Rublyovka to Kapotnya and the giant slash in the monthly allotted sum he received from the capital. Eight long years of pinching rubles at every corner and living at the bare minimum. Eight long years of saving every ruble he could manage. How foreign was this to him! Living scrupulously instead of lavishly! *If only my father could see me now. From king of the free world to a lonely old hermit living in squalor and poverty on the teat of the Russian bear.* he thought to himself. What would his father think about what this money was being saved for, he wondered? Would he approve of this futile effort to grab on to youth one more time or would he condemn him for an old man's folly? It didn't matter now. Nothing could shake his resolve. He figured if he went on this week and the next eating only one small meal a day when next month's stipend came through, he would finally have enough money to accomplish his last wish. One last night of warmth before the icy embrace of death. Donald knew his old body well enough that he was confident in the fact he could survive on this poor man's regiment the next few weeks. How he was going to feed himself after this night didn't matter to him. Nothing other than this night mattered to him. He felt death already. The nearness of him the last few years had almost turned into a comfort. Only the attainment of youthful beauty once more kept him clinging to the meager existence he has been scrapping out these last eight years. But what he craved wasn't just the illusion of youthful beauty brought on by his favorite escorts during his few years in Rublyovka; it was true youth's beauty! The purity of adolescents only found in virginity. And it was this desire, one warm night with a beautiful, young virgin, which had taken eight long, patient years of going hungry and cold saving his rubles to obtain.

***

Kapotnya had a thriving Tochka. Old Man Trump had befriended a few of the older madams that ran the district a couple years back in hopes that he would actually reach the moment at hand. Having thoroughly explained to them who he was and what they were looking for, they were glad to oblige. He had laid out everything to them, his whole life's story leading up to what he hoped would be his final act on the planet. He spent most of his time on this green Earth with his grubby little fingers draining youth like a vampire from the beautiful women he surrounded himself with. Now that he stood in front of death, face to face, he was certain how he wanted to be taken: just how he lived. Surrounded by young, beautiful women. Or at least a young, beautiful woman.

The arrangements were made a few months ago. The madams had even helped him figure out a budget to fit his time table. They were just as aware as he was how sensitive his time was and being able to sell the same young girl's virginity twice was, up until this point, something the madams could have never imagined was possible. An opportunity like this, with a man like him, could not be passed up.

He was promised a very beautiful virgin of a nondescript age. Knowing how far along into girlhood the maiden was would somehow tamper with the magic of the night. He knew he would fixate more on the young age of the girl herself than the youth that she embodied, becoming hung up on the simulacra of this youth and robbed of the last comfort he was in search of. He also took other very extensive precautions to all but eliminate the possibility of him confusing anything that was going to transpire between him and the little miss for its simulation. He wanted the girl drugged and put to sleep in order to guarantee her compliance with all his light touches and careful caresses. A slight shudder or a misplaced whimper on her part would ruin it all for him. The madams had pushed back on this at first, but, after a few months of time with Old Man Trump, they conceded to his whims, coming to the understanding that this decrepit, geriatric soul harbored no ill will toward womankind. In fact, it was just the opposite; they had soon realised how much he venerated women. The last bits of hypermasculinity he was so accustomed to most of his life only hung on to his character here, with his desire and respect for that perennial beauty which is female. The madams were able to differentiate between these types of masculine manifestations and those of more toxic hypermasculine men. The kind of men who suffered from both misogyny and a sex addiction. It was their trade, after all, and they were experts. Seeing him for who he was, they felt an almost gleeful accomplishment of duty when they went about searching for the right maiden.

The girl was to be dressed in order for him to take the time to undress her. He wanted the girl asleep when he entered the room. He also wanted the girl to sleep through the morning. She was to never see his face. An electric blanket, a fresh pair of sheets, a king-size bed, and a nice steak were the last things he asked to have accompanied. A young, beautiful virgin had been found for him. They agreed to all his demands and the date was set for the evening he received his next stipend.

***

That night was especially cold. Death had stopped lurking in Old Man Trump's shadow and was now walking beside him in silence, as if they were ancient lovers. He pulled his Toscana coat up above his face to shield his cheeks from the bite of the wind. The icy air bared down on him harder than ever before. He was utterly surprised by this. The thought of the night to come should have filled him with that youthful warmth he missed so. He had hoped the chill that spread from his appendages into his very existence itself would dissipate as he got closer to the little shack in the street adjacent to the tochka in which they agreed to meet. The opposite happened. The longer he walked, the colder he got. He felt a few close brushes with death, but persevered regardless. Nothing would stop him now. He was too close to his goal. He would stave off death for as long as it took if he had to. Right now, he sought beauty in its most purest existence, and not even the gods themselves could stop him.

The madams greeted him at the door and rushed him inside, out of the elements, with great haste. They couldn't shut the door fast enough to keep death outside. They had watched him walk in with the old man and couldn't hide the horror on their faces. "Are you sure you want to do this?" they asked him. "It looks like it's going to kill you." But Donald insisted. They wouldn't be so cruel to deny a dying old man his last wish, especially after they went to all the trouble to find a girl and already accepted payment. If the girl wasn't already asleep, it would be a different story. "If I pass through the night, I don't want to know what you're going to do with my body." The madams voiced their discomfort at this, but didn't resist for long. This was the world they lived in. Sudden death under their roof wasn't a foreign concept to them.

They offered the old man a cup of coffee to warm his spirits, which he accepted and drank down greedily. After a few cups, he decided it was time to meet his night's companion. One of the madams said the girl was asleep in the bedroom at the top of the shack. She took him as far as the top of the steps, helping him along the way, and left him to his own devices.

Old Man Trump lingered just outside the room, peering through the crack in the door trying to make out the silhouette of the young girl. An old aluminum desk lamp sat on the bed stand beside her and illuminated her enough that Donald could make out her features under the electric blanket. Her hair was a light strawberry blonde. It hid most of her face and spiderwebbed across her shoulder, over her back, and down along the covers. Dark roots were barely visible in the light and he couldn't tell if the blonde hair was fake or natural. He would never know the color of her eyes. Turning over in her sleep, the shapely form of the young girl became visible for the first time. The blanket was pulled below her navel when she moved. Her midriff was toned just slightly. *Maybe she was some kind of athlete,* he thought to himself. Perky little tits budded off her chest, just barely filling out her slip. They seemed as if they were still growing right in front of him. His eyes followed her torso up to her slender collarbones. The old man almost thought for a moment that she sensed his presence standing there just outside the room and was about to wake in front of him, greet him at the door, and pull him by the hand into the bed beside her. But she only turned over. He stood outside the door for another minute or two before he was sure the girl was really asleep and not just pretending to be.

Walking over to the bed, he shut the lamp off and sat down beside the girl mere inches away from her but not touching her just yet. He wanted to give his eyes the chance to adjust to the dark. The lamp was dim and he was staring into the room long enough that his eyes got used to the darkness quickly, even for his old age. Her smell was the first thing to grab him. It was the warm smell of youth. Older, though, then he had first assumed since she lacked the milky scent of a babe and carried with her the faint scent of a woman fully grown. He felt the coldness that had been burrowing deeper and deeper into his bones start to subside. Relief came only for an instant, because in a moment of weakness, Old Man Trump started to reflect on what he was about to do.

Could there be anything uglier than an old man lying the night through beside a girl put to sleep, unwaking? Had he not come to this old house seeking the ultimate in the ugliness of old age?

And the reality that this girl was asleep and would not stir or react at his touch started to eat at him. He knew the necessity of her being asleep for his ultimate goal, but still, the fact that she slept there without even an idea of the old man sitting next to her filled Donny with a sudden rage. He thought about striking the girl hard across the face to see if she would respond to him. He thought about grabbing her and screaming in her face to wake up while he shook her violently. He thought about violating her with his fingers, his toes, with the lamp, or anything else he could find in the room. He cursed himself for his old age and incontinence. If it wasn't for that, he would have just raped the fucking bitch where she lie. That thought disturbed him enough to pull him back into this room and out of his head. *No need to let things like this eat away at me,* he thought to himself in disgust. The feelings of rage were replaced with ones of sorrow and loneliness from his old age. The dark walls began to envelope him. He felt the room breathing around him; an uneven pulsing began to throb on the floor below his feet.

The young girl stirred again and scooted tight against him, wrapping an arm around his waist. Heavy thuds sounded like a cacophony against the small of his back. A soothing rhythm could be heard through her chest cavity. He felt blessed at this. Soon, her heartbeat was drowning out everything else that existed in the room. This heartbeat had brought eroticism and death together in his mind as an inseparable entity. He felt the cold hand of the Reaper come to rest on his shoulder and knew that was his old friend granting him permission to satisfy one last vice.

Old Man Trump slipped both his hands under the young girl's slip and slowly peeled it off her skin, over her small breasts, and off her head. Her blonde hair tickled his hand as he brushed it out of her face in order to get a really good look at her features. Her cheekbones were high and pronounced; they sucked her cheeks into her mouth and left her lips pursed together, as if in a kiss. The old man took that as an invite and let his lips taste hers for the first time in the night. He could taste the medicine on her lips and wondered what they had given her to put her to sleep like this. Her skin was soft, so soft against the paper skin he had all along his body. There was a struggle undoing her bra strap. His hands weren't as nimble as they used to be and shook in fits with his age. Little pink nipples shot off the tips of her tits. He gave the one a light pinch at first. The girl paid him no mind. Then he started twisting rougher, pulling on them in every direction. Still, she laid there undisturbed. Panties went next. He couldn't make out the color in the dark, but they felt like lace and were nothing more than a few little strings stitched together. The coarse layer of hair above her crotch was black. Well, that settled it; the blonde hair on her head was fake after all. The faint scent of her sex wafted up toward him, and it was at that moment he realized the cold that had stuck with him in his bones wasn't nearly as strong. Whatever life was hiding in the sleeping girl seeped into the old man.

He spent the majority of the next few hours covering her body in kisses, fondling every inch of her, and trying to capture as much of her youthful beauty in his mind's eye in order to be able to take it with him after the night. Her hip bones showed through her skin, protruding out of her waist as an inviting reminder for the fertile, untouched womb that lay underneath.

Finally, he had attained that which had eluded him since his exile! Glory to he who acquires both the patience to suppress and satiate one's own ego. Glory to the eternal attainment of youth and beauty! And here, he had captured both of these things and held them suspended in a state of stasis in front of him. A newfound appreciation, an almost insatiable lust, for what he had lost with his old age overtook him and filled him with an almost drunken stupor.

The intoxicating aroma of her youth was more exhausting than he could have realized. Exhaustion took hold of him in a way he never experienced before. The slow musical rhythm of the young girl's heartbeat reminded him of a soft lullaby his nanny used to sing him to sleep with. Death once again placed his cold hand on Old Man Trump's shoulder, giving him permission for one last wish before they went off together into the cold, cold night.

The old man stood up and walked to the empty side of the bed. He stripped off his nightgown and underwear while he slipped into bed next to the young beauty. The covers swallowed the bodies up like the earth as they came together in one final embrace.

Here he laid in the presence of youthful beauty, the warmth of this unknown young girl coursing through his old veins. His labored breath clashed against hers in an unnatural harmony. Soon, though, his old heart had matched the beating of her much younger, stronger one. It was at that moment that he fell asleep with the young girl wrapped tightly in his arms.

Not long after did the Old Man pass in his sleep. His feeble heart could only keep up with the rapid flutters of the young beauties for so long before it gave out. When he didn't come down the stairs in the morning, the madams knew what had happened. Moving with great quickness, they rushed up the steps and saw what they feared most but knew was waiting for them. The young girl still laid there asleep in the arms of the cold and lifeless old man. Who knows how long they had laid there in this perverse position. The older women didn't want to think about it. They swore there that they would never mention this to the young girl. As hard as they tried, they could not pry the maiden out of the old man's clutches. His limbs clung to her body stiff and heavy, nigh unmovable, like a forest of old oak whose roots have burrowed deep into the Earth.

The old whores had to grab their pimps to dispose of the old man, for they lacked the strength. Laboring, the men were finally able to pry the youth from the dead. They rolled him up in an old, grey rug that laid on the downstairs floor and into the back of a van. The madams didn't know where the men took the bodies they needed disposed of; they didn't want to know. They knew the night before they were probably going to be here this morning. Still, death rarely greets you in quite the way you expect it to, and in this regard, the madams felt a pang of jealousy and a newfound respect for the Old Man, who had not only greeted death in his own way, but planned the journey into the afterlife with Death himself as his companion.

THE EMPEROR'S GAMBIT

by Faisal Marzipan

The emperor did that little dance he always does, shaking his hips side to side while moving his hands in a perfect figure eight (infinity?) motion and pointing at members in the audience. The red and chilly rock behind him was a startling contrast to his power suit, though at least the tie matched. Then he flashed that wry charming smile of his.

"The haters and critics said it could never be done, but here we are in 2040, and I tell ya, we've only just begun."

They cheated him, and made it obvious, but the gambit Trump made was that he would allow the vaccine to take hold, and in a whisper campaign of mommy bloggers and right-wing bodybuilders, he would allow enforcement to turn a blind eye to those who opted out. The mRNA vaccine itself proved far more dangerous than the disease. It was a conspiracy of dunces, really just two Malthusian virologists slaving away at the behest of an overly earnest bureaucracy working at warp speed. The translational mutations took a month to reach critical mass; by that time, the global rollout was complete. The spike mutation produces odd nodules, and even, on occasion, horns in offspring. Newborns were horribly disfigured, had heart conditions, and would screech in hideous, rapturous wails. The newborns were so abhorrent that Pope Benedict XVII (formerly Cardinal Sarah) pronounced that, "In spite of the reverent approach of the One Holy Church towards the issues of life, the demonic nature of this vaccine is an affront to nature." Democrats took the vaccine religiously and roughly half died of grand mal seizures; Bell's palsy was just the icing on the cake.

The whisper campaign of bodybuilding Twitter and mommy bloggers held out in the West, but the third world had succumbed to the Gates Foundation's massive rollout. By March, the counter-coup was over, and despite pockets of West Coast resistance, the United States converted from a republic to a formal empire, and the Emperor became who he was meant to be. DeSantis, Rudy, Robert Kraft, and Dan Patrick (of Texas) mobilized hubs of regional authority after the Senate was dissolved. The stock market eclipsed previous highs on news of the Emperor's victory.

Junior headed up the Make Africa Great program. It was an attempt to enlighten the Dark Continent, involving 100,000 Nordic bodybuilders breeding nonstop up to eight African women a day. The women were selected for fertility, maternal nature, aesthetics, and intelligence. Now, 20 years later, the MAG program is beginning to bear its first fruits, with the new generation of bodybuilding mulattos trained in ancient Greek and raised in Benedictine monasteries or Calvinist enclaves. They demonstrate exceptional table manners and yet can still shoot a basketball. Trainmaster Alex designed an extensive railway program modeled after Tokyo, in Johannesburg, that would tie the continent together, and finally, Cecil Rhodes' dream could be realized.

Jared and Ivanka made aliyah, as did much of the Orthodox Jewish community. Jared assumed leadership of Israel after Netanyahu resigned. They made several peace deals throughout the region in the last 20 years. It was a shame what happened to Iran, but it was too close to many Israeli military bases in Iraq, Syria, and Afghanistan. Sometimes, Ivanka would help create new countries, such as Kurdistan, just so they could be recognized by Israel. The greatest peace deals, really.

Eric Trump ventured to Brazil and made a partnership with Bolsonaro, which was the greatest deal in the history of South America, much greater than even the Treaty of Madrid. Brazil retained sovereignty and mineral rights to Bolivian natural gas, and the remainder of South America was rebranded to the Trump-Exxon Tropical Exhibit and Resource Extraction Zone. Chile had specials on helicopter rides. For modest protection fees to Eric, the former countries of the zone could retain some autonomy. The original Coca-Cola recipe was revived with Columbian cocaine and the fentanyl warehouses were put out of business. There was a massive shift in productivity.

China's biggest and only export was glass.

To those who chose to remain in their cocoons, listen to cable news, and binge watch self-caponized refugee coming of age stories, Trump was never their president, and they never could envision an emperor. They adopted a "loser takes none" mentality. The reality they wished to adopt embraced them like a warm opioid buzz. The facts on the ground never entered their consciousness. Their cats became feral. But here, above ground, the world needed to keep running, and Trump's mastery of the OODA loop was never more valuable. In 2030, around the same time Barron was elevated to the throne of the New Holy Roman Empire, Elon convinced Trump to upload his consciousness to the cloud. Trump naturally balked.

"Look, I said, I may be 83, but I'm sharp as a tack. Good genes, like my father," he told Elon.

"But Emperor Trump, you cannot be everywhere at once, and this allows you to give speeches, fundraisers without even having to be there. Unless...you like traveling?"

That was enough to convince the emperor. He did multiple whole-brain physiology scans, EEG, MRI, PET scans. Rorschach tests, blood tests. The result was a nearly perfect replica. They had the holograms down pat as well, smooth transitions of movement with no weird opacity issues. Trump was asked to speak in a conversational and rhetorical tone, and GANs were generated based on events of the day. Then, Elon did something remarkable: he downloaded Donald Trump's consciousness into the AI network of his Tesla Gigafactory. Tech nerds called it a Trumpularity event, while normal folk simply claimed that Trump gave the AI some intuition, or maybe gumption. The androids, which were not humanoid in any sense, nonetheless began manufacturing self-driving rockets in benevolent service to humanity. Their goal was to terraform Mars. And now, here in 2040, was Emperor Trump (or at least a convincing facsimile) to encourage them.

"And so, my people were nervous, they said, 'Sir, Sir, you can't just terraform Mars, it doesn't have an atmosphere.'" Trump stopped impersonating his pessimistic assistant. "I said, 'Okay, so what do you need to generate an atmosphere? Carbon dioxide? We got more carbon dioxide than we know what to do with, just freeze the extra,' and, you see, we make more carbon dioxide on Earth than we need, and if we believe in global warming, so I said, 'Freeze it and send it to Mars.' Do you know how they make carbonated soda? You freeze the carbon dioxide and you put it in water. Boom, it's like magic.

"Then, later on, my people, they come to me and they say, 'Sir, sir, the solar wind will blow away the carbon dioxide.' So, I said to them, 'How do you keep an atmosphere from blowing away?' and they said, 'Sir, you need a magnetosphere.'"

Fake and dying news networks were aware of the GANs and were using their own GANs to "pre-bunk" the President's statements before he could make them, the crawl along the feed showing, "This statement about the necessity of magnetospheres has been disputed."

But Emperor Trump persisted. "TKX-1356, are you there? TKX, where are you pal? Everyone give this service module a hand. He does great work." The androids simulate applause. "So it was TKX-1356 that told me, 'Mr. President, sir, Mars has a molten iron core, it just needs to move to generate a dipole for creating a magnetosphere.' And, so, you know this is not my specialty; I mean, I'm just a real estate guy, but you know, if you have a magnetic field and enough carbon dioxide, you can have two habitable planets instead of zero. And if we're exporting excess carbon dioxide...look, I'm not saying, but we have so much oil, and so much beautiful clean coal. Why not burn it here on Mars and generate all the precious carbon dioxide we NEED on Mars to generate an atmosphere?

"And so I asked TK, I call him TK, I said, 'TK, just how are we going to get the molten core to move to create this dipole?'

"And he told me, this beautiful process, that just changing the temperature at various locations throughout the crust, imagine this now, just a few changes in crust temperature in the millikelvins (by the way, do you know how small millikelvins are?)..."

The pre-buttals and pre-bunking algorithms contradicted him constantly, the frame around his beautiful, pristine visage turned glowing red with a "pants on fire" indicator, but this feed was only accepted by the entombed, kombucha-embalmed binge watchers. "Ex-President Trump Rants on Mars," screamed the chyron petulantly. The pre-bunkings would state, for example, there was NO excess carbon dioxide on Earth. The androids here on Mars needed the pre-buttals and debunking information, which optimized their productivity. GAN stands for generative adversarial network, which works by having a generative layer (in this case, the emperor) and a discriminative layer (here, the rebuttals and debunking). The adversarial nature of this programming was crucial to Trump's success. The androids were already installing multiple Tesla-branded crust-temperature fluctuators.

"We are gonna have the most beautiful bow field, and believe me, I've seen some in my time. We are gonna create the most beautiful resort here at Jezero Crater. The haters and critics said it could never be done, but I'm here, and you're here, and together, we are going to make Mars' Atmosphere Great Again for humanity and androids. God bless you and God bless Mars."

Back in Trump Tower, Emperor Trump watches the end of the speech. At 93, he is still spry, though reserved.

"I gave a great speech there. And trust me, I know. I've given many, many speeches in my day."

"Yes, dahling," replied Melania.

"They said it could have been done, that it was impossible."

"I know, dahling."

Emperor Trump then reaches over and turns off the Melania projector as a single tear wells up in that beautiful, generous eye of his. The soft poignant moment of regret, the one thing never uploaded to the GANs.

DONALD TRUMP AND THE SPIRIT OF DEMOCRACY

by the Flaming Eyeball

When considering what will happen in the future, it is important to consider what we know and do not know about the present. I do not know who will sit in the Oval Office on January 22nd. If it is President Trump, I do not know what path he will choose to remain, whether he will ascend by laws of paper or of iron. I liken Americans' situation right now to an audience in a theater who has just seen the end of a famous play gone wrong. The actors are senile and their lines never came out right. Behind them, the set was collapsing. The show supposedly ended, but we can now see rustling behind the curtains. This essay concerns not what is happening behind the scenes, which most people cannot know, but what is going on in the audience: the astonishment of the theatergoers, the tension in the air. Remember that one of the biggest events in American history was a play gone off script, and that when the smoke cleared, our nation was changed forever.

Theater, in fact, is a perfect metaphor for liberal democracy. The faces the audience sees are not the ones that control the show. For every actor, there are dozens of crew members, directors, musicians, and others in the background, and owners and shareholders behind them. Similarly, in liberal democracy, the voters see the politicians, but they don't see the bureaucrats, poll workers, and party staff who form and shape our government, nor the lobbyists and donors who control the system through their money. Moldbug called this phenomenon the Cathedral, but he might as well have called it the Theater, for the ordinary people inside it act not like worshippers but like role-playing members of an interactive charade called representative democracy.

The role of the president within this theater is as a kind of stage king. When you ask the question "who rules America?" most people will say "the president," because that is who they see giving the speeches and who holds the nominal power. Like in any good play, the other actors on stage have their own desires and lines, but in the end, the king will make a deal with Congress and get things done. Of course, things are more complicated. Deals don't get made onstage; the actors onstage don't do the bidding of the people who supposedly sent them there, yet there are still consistent policies pushed to further the interests of the men behind the curtain.

This is all common knowledge on this side of the Internet, to the point of being a platitude. What people forget is the PURPOSE of the whole charade. A Cathedral without worshippers is just a building, likewise a Theater without an audience. The whole Cathedral's legitimacy stems from the appearance that elected representatives of We the People make laws with the consent of the governed, and other unelected officials (who are still representative) will wisely enforce those laws. It stems from people trusting the news to keep them "informed citizens" of either the red team or the blue team, and trusting at least one team enough to root for it. It stems from Americans believing in the idea that ultimately, laws rule our country and not men, like the other great powers of history. It stems from the idea that our voices matter and our votes count; even if you don't like the law, the script goes, an average citizen like you can work within the system to elect politicians who will change it, and if enough other citizens are concerned, it will happen. The audience must participate for any of it to make sense, because they think it's their show.

Here is my thesis: despite all the talk of Trump as an American Caesar or a king, he is in fact the last gasp of real democracy in our country. He may use illiberal means to reach power, but his claim to legitimacy is that he is the true winner of the election, which was stolen by an irredeemably broken system. Conversely, the Cathedral uses the paper laws of "our democracy" to install a senile puppet as a skinsuit for the tyranny of various moneyed interests. To continue the theater analogy, the audience is realizing amidst the turmoil who actually controls the show. Trump is not a military Caesar: he is a popular actor on Broadway playing Shakespeare's

Caesar. The audience is watching him be betrayed not only by the senators on stage, but by the stage crew and the owners of the theater, who have a vendetta against the actor's life. The crowd is preparing to swarm the stage to save their star. This is Trump's primary strength: as Sidney Powell once said, the entire system is against Trump and the only ones who support the Trump team are his supporters, the American people.

The most important essay on the election so far has been Yarvin's "Vae Victis," which points out this naked power grab is nothing less than the Cathedral putting a stop to the show. In that essay, Yarvin points out that election fraud is not new in American history and that it needs to be accepted as a potential factor in the election. Yet here is the difference between fraud in the past and the steal of 2020. Election fraud in the past was usually corrupt urban machines exerting their power over their region, or else a thumb on the scale, such as in 1960 or 2000. In other words, the general system could maintain its legitimacy while fraud could either be written off as "just a New York/Chicago thing" or else maintain plausible deniability. But in 2020, any narrative of how fraud happened must include a vast conspiracy, which implicates, at a minimum, election officials in half a dozen states, state and local legislatures and governments, judges, and billionaire donors who are all complicit in stealing the presidential election while nonetheless allowing the Republican Party to gain House seats and state legislatures. The entire apparatus of the American government is implicated in such a belief, which almost every Trump supporter holds, and Stacey Abrams is now bragging about stealing the Senate in January. The Cathedral has never unmasked itself in such a way before: it does not care at all about the people it has just disenfranchised, but humiliates and insults them further.

To show you how egregiously the Cathedral has revealed itself, let's go over the timeline of the past few months. Many states had implemented vast new mail-in systems (famously low-integrity, and banned in many other countries) to supposedly fight COVID-19. Huge numbers of dubiously verified ballots came in before and after the election date. The night of the election, Trump was winning overall until the water pipe supposedly burst in Atlanta and there was a pause in six different states, after which huge numbers of Biden votes come in and flipped him the vote. (For reference, sudden pauses in counting votes have been the cause of violent revolution and civil war in various nations.) After this, despite many obvious anomalies, recorded videos, and eyewitnesses, no one in the entire Democratic Party has ever once bothered to try to explain any part of Biden's sketchy "victory" at all. To the contrary, they have treated anyone remotely skeptical of the results with the utmost scorn. Poll workers gave election monitors no way to observe, cheered as they were escorted out of the room, and in one case gave them bracelets with poop emojis on them to mark who they were. Social media outlets and YouTube censored news relating to election fraud, and the Biden campaign hired foreign shills to flood the Internet with pro-Biden memes and messages. The Republican state officials waffled but were ultimately impotent, even as the entire judiciary, including the Supreme Court, threw out almost all lawsuits without once hearing evidence. Now, state officials are destroying evidence, resisting subpoenas, and defying court orders. The Uniparty doesn't give a damn about the law, or anything but collectively obtaining power.

As Yarvin said, the Democrats stole this one fair and square. The game is rigged, the ref has been bought, one team's players have decided to blow the game, and the umpire is looking the other way. The institutions of liberal democracy are giving results that are certified and verified as the truth by all the other institutions as all contestation is dismissed. The letter of the law supports Biden, for the investigators declare that the procedure was followed and the judges found nothing wrong with the results.

The problem, as Mark Twain said, was not what the government didn't declare, but what they did declare that just wasn't so. Censoring knowledge in an ostensibly liberal society with Internet access isn't easy; even from the beginning, it was obvious to millions of people that the election was stolen. Fox News didn't report on election fraud, so half their audience left for OANN and Newsmax. Shills flooded 4chan, but the anons there still did statistical analysis and news reporting. Twitter put "fact-checking" labels on all kinds of Tweets, but people still got the news out anyway. Against the entire centralized media and government apparatus arose an army of Facebook boomers, anonymous autists, and independent investigators. They were greatly aided by the public hearings in different states, along with the actions of Trump himself. And they helped a new and powerful counter-narrative take root among Trump's supporters.

These people are at least 45 percent of the country and 70 million people, they are convinced the system is fundamentally illegitimate, they are some of the most productive people in America, and they are not going away. The powers that be have taken every step imaginable to ostracize and torment them: close their businesses, cause chaos and crime, destroy their monuments, slander their entire history and race. Quite frankly, I believe this insulting stimulus bill was the last straw, rubbing everyone's nose in the fact that our leaders of both parties care more about faraway countries and ensuring cheap labor than they do their own people. The spirit of 1776 is in the air; today alone, Republicans broke into the state house of Oregon while standing off with cops and beating up journalists, and almost every Republican I have met is calling for violence, even if they are not yet very good at inflicting it. The most law-abiding and industrious people on Earth have awoken from their slumber, and what Donald Trump represents is nothing less than the spirit of democracy over the corrupt traitors who have usurped its law.

And who are these leaders who stand against the American people? We are ruled by geriatric narcissists who believe they will live forever; look at the various oligarchs and realize that a majority of them are over the median American life expectancy. Nancy Pelosi is 80, Klaus Schwab is 82, George Soros is 90. For God's sake, Henry Kissinger, who was just fired by Trump, is 97 years old! The irony of the oligarchs titling their project "Great Reset 2030" is the fact that most of the resetters themselves will not be alive to see it come to fruition. No, it is the last gasp of a dying order, the last attempt by feeble and dying men to keep their grip on the world, not by the strength of their faded hands but by poisoning everyone until we are all too weak to resist. In America, they cannot use much force; they can assassinate individuals, shoot up compounds like Waco, and hire felons and junkies to start riots, but even a hundred organized men like Cliven Bundy's militias will force them to back down in the end. And this is why these oligarchs hate and fear the brotherhood of men. It is why America's laws regulating estrogenic chemicals in the environment are weaker not only than Europe's but China's, why our food is filled with poison and our media with sterile sexuality, why our "education" demoralizes, and why our streets are filled with strangers. It is why they will try to overthrow any government which does not follow them; one of Biden's first policy priorities will be to overthrow the governments of Hungary, Poland, and Brazil. Because these oligarchs are parasites who can only rule over an inverted order.

But the old tricks don't work anymore, because the husks of the institutions of democracy no longer inspire anyone. The oligarchs depend upon the lies to be able to rule at all, the lies that Trump's landslide victory has expelled forever in the hearts of his supporters. If you think that this makes no difference, look at Ceausescu in Romania: he ruled with an iron fist until one day, the Soviet Union was discredited, people lost respect for him, and lynched him. When you look at how America is ruled right now, consider that so far there has been pretty much no right-wing political violence at all, despite less aid given than anywhere else in the developed world. But the conservatives no longer trust the police, nor do they trust their state or national governments: they only trust Trump. Again, the Cathedral has done nothing but spite, provoke, and starve them, to the point that many of them will be forced to resort to violence simply to be able to open their businesses again. People in dissident circles are afraid that there will be a false-flag attack blamed on "white supremacists," but at this point, I suspect that if someone (including a federal agent) shot up a CNN building or even the Michigan governor's office, they would be revered and not hated by Trump's supporters, sort of like the sheriff who semi-endorsed the militia members in Michigan a few months ago when they plotted to kidnap the governor. It would only take several dozen angry, armed people to hold an entire legislative meeting hostage; a mob did this a few months ago in Armenia and assaulted the speaker of their parliament after losing their war with Azerbaijan. (Just in case there is any confusion, I am not endorsing violence.)

This outburst of democratic spirit in Trump's post-election movement coincides with the point at which democracy cannot be trusted anymore by the majority of people. Every election in the past ten years or more is now suspect. The American republic is dead because it no longer commands the allegiance of the majority. Accordingly, the left is DEAD as a creative force, existing only as a specter to exercise power. It can still muscle through things it wants, but it has no solutions to the problems of our day and is still fundamentally loyal to the current order. If Trump wins, leftism is crushed, and if Biden is president, it is still crushed; there are no Bernie supporters in Biden's cabinet, only vultures. The only real way forward is on the right. There will be two main factions in American politics from now on: conservatives who believe in the Constitution as an ideal despite hating the current institutions, and right-wingers who reject the

Constitution and wish to replace it. These two will work together against the oligarchs, but the Constitution and the question of how our country ought to be ruled will be the main debate in American politics.

The conservatives will be sort of like the modern Communist Party in Russia: older people who remember the old ways and want to go back to them, in this case back to when the American republic still ran right. They may support martial law in the short term, but the idea of liberal democracy still appeals to them, even if only as nostalgia. The latter wing is still emerging. It will be comprised of a combination of many movements: former Republican rejects like paleocons, conservatives who changed their minds, and elements of the far right, to name a few. This faction will suffer from great internal contradictions, but will support using some kind of strongman to represent the interests of the people. This faction will also be helped by the fact that relatively few people under the age of 40 strongly support democracy as an ideal. Trump, though belonging to the first faction, will be an inspiration to the second if he stays in power; even if he doesn't go full Putin, he will warm people to the idea of a centralized leader.

Following this, normal Republicans right now are adrift. They support President Trump and they want to follow him. Many would die for him, like the caller on Rush Limbaugh's show. But their world is falling apart before their eyes. The GOP has been revealed as obvious controlled opposition, and everything these people thought they knew turned out to be wrong. And this is where the various sections of the online right must and will come in. Yarvin correctly mentioned that Republican leaders have the souls of real estate agents. No one has ever taught your average Republican how to be brave or face adversity, and many are physically obese from decades of poor nutrition. But they mean well, and they will reach out to anyone who has answers. They have all kinds of questions and have opened up almost overnight to suggestions. Why is it so hard to lose weight? Who really controls our country? Why is everything so ugly nowadays? How can we be courageous and have faith? This is how a real right-wing movement is built and is a tremendous opportunity for anyone to educate and spread simple messages.

I conclude by stating that the nominally democratic institutions of our day neither represent the will of the American people nor our interests.

Trump, by contrast, represents both by fighting the oligarchs. Trump is therefore the last champion of democracy in America, for the American electoral system will never again enjoy the universal prestige that it used to. Trump will go down in history as one of the most consequential American presidents alongside Lincoln and FDR: whether he stays in power or not, he will have presided over an enormous transition of the structure of the American government, representing the ultimate gasp of the republic's promise of government "of the people, by the people, for the people."

VINDICATED

by Wurtweakle

I had a strange dream last night.

I was lying on my back with my eyes closed. I slowly opened them. The sky was a deep, grayish purple color, with black streaks like little worms wriggling through the air. There was a howling wind, cold and bitter, and thunder and lightning roared. I tried to get up, but I was paralyzed up to my neck. With great effort, I lifted up my head and looked around. A mass of bodies lay on the cold asphalt, black as night. I could feel it now, like laying on a block of ice, or a cold sheet of metal.

They all wore the same clothes: a baseball cap, a T-shirt, and basketball shorts. The clothes were mostly colored red or blue, with the occasional yellow, green, purple, or white.

On one of the shirts was a red "X" from shoulder to waist. I looked down at my own body. For some reason, I wasn't wearing what everyone else was. I was wearing my usual blue suit, white undershirt, and red tie, with a small American flag pin on my right side, beige dress pants, and black dress shoes.

Then suddenly, a trumpet blast was heard, and I was able to stand up. I could see the White House in the distance, levitating in the air. Then all the people surrounding me woke up and stared at me with wide eyes. After a moment, they all started to make a path for me, towards the White House. I began walking. I saw a man pushing through the great mass of people to get to me. As he came closer, I finally recognized his face.

Mike.

His first name was all I could remember about him. That and the fact that I had known him at some point in time.

He had short white hair and a solemn yet determined look on his face.

When he reached me, he pulled out his hand for a handshake. His hand was firm and confident. He looked me in the eye and said softly:

"All will be revealed."

We reached the White House. I looked to my left and in the distance, an old man in a wheelchair pushed by a woman was approaching. For some reason, they looked familiar, but I couldn't quite remember who they were. The old man had white hair and a quilted blanket on his lap. The woman had an unnerving smile that sent shivers down my spine. I looked to my right and saw a black man with very short black hair and a short beard. Behind him were about a hundred other people with blurred faces, except for one woman wearing a yellow dress, who was carrying a porcupine.

Mr. West.

Again, I could only remember the name of the black man, the last name this time. And one strange phrase came into my head:

You should be honored by my lateness.

After about a minute, the two parties had reached me.

Suddenly, a great light flashed from the White House above. We all looked up and saw a man standing on the steps with a black beard with some grey in it.

I remembered he was some sort of government man. A Republican, I think.

He lifted up his right hand and extended his index finger straight upward into the sky.

"Bring out…the ballots," he said in a loud Texan accent.

I felt an urge to look upward and did so. Gracefully descending from the heavens were over a hundred 18-wheeler delivery trucks. When they landed on the ground, they exploded into an ocean of paper. When all the trucks had fallen, the sea of paper was lifted into the air, sorted, and placed into several wooden boxes with slots.

There were two large boxes, three smaller boxes, and about a few hundred even smaller boxes about the size of a radio. The boxes had white labels. The one to my left read "BIDEN." The one to my right: "TRUMP."

My name.

Suddenly, memories of my presidency rushed before my mind. In my final year, there was some sort of flu going around. A black man had died on the side of a road and suddenly entire city blocks were on fire, stores were looted, and people were shot dead.

I tried to remember if I had won my reelection campaign, But my mind came up blank. The last thing my mind could remember was me standing before a massive crowd the day before election day, Michigan I think, with all the people crying out "WE LOVE YOU" over and over again.

On top of the ballot boxes were two floating numbers, one of top of the other. The top number had "EC" next to it, the bottom one "PV." Suddenly, a gigantic map of the United States appeared in the sky. As the ballots flew into the boxes, the map filled in red and blue. The whole process took about ten minutes. When it was finished, my side read "EC 232, PV 74,210,833" and the Biden side said "EC 306, PV 81,270,009."

I turned to the old man; he was smiling intently.

For some odd reason, I could smell cigar smoke. Then, out of nowhere, I heard "NOT ON MY WATCH!" said in a crisp Italian accent.

I looked up and saw a man levitating above me. He had a big Cuban cigar in his mouth.

He looked down on me and waved. I instinctively waved back. I turned to the old man in the wheelchair and saw his smile had faded. The woman was scowling, her yellow teeth showing.

I looked back up to the cigar man. He slowly closed his eyes, gritted his teeth, lowered his head, and clenched his fists.

Suddenly, ballots were flowing out of the Biden ballot box and into my own. I looked up at the map and suddenly saw that Georgia had turned from blue to red. Next came Pennsylvania, then Wisconsin, then Michigan, then Arizona, then Nevada...

I looked down to my ballot box. The numbers now read "EC 296," But the PV number was blurred.

The world around me was fading. The Texan man floated downwards, got right into my face, looked me straight in the eye, and said, "You will be vindicated, Donald."

Then I woke up.

I was sweating profusely. I looked at my clock. "2:32 AM," it read. I was in my bedroom at the Mar-a-Lago.

I never conceded the race, but I was forced out of the White House on that fateful January day. The Secret Service had turned on me. Months had passed since then. My Twitter was suspended a couple weeks after. There were mass riots going on.

Cases of the virus had skyrocketed despite the vaccine. Biden had attempted to implement the most draconian lockdown imaginable. Certain red states were attempting to secede from the Union. The world was going to hell.

But I knew one thing was certain:

I was going to be vindicated.

UNCLE JOHN'S LEGACY

by Hans G. Schwartz

"Barron," croaked the old man. "Glad you made it."

"I came as soon as I heard," his son replied, still breathing heavily from the fast pace he took navigating through the Trump Presidential Library Annex at Mar-a-Lago.

The former president's head turned slowly on the crisp white linen of the pillow to face the nurse. "Leave us."

The nurse's eyes focused on the president's vital signals. She glared disapprovingly back at her patient a moment before yielding to the inevitable. "Try not to excite him," she cautioned Barron. "I'll be just outside if he needs me." She stepped out, closing the door behind her.

Barron surveyed the replica of the Oval Office, painstakingly reproduced to match its configuration during his father's presidency. "You made them wheel your hospital bed in here?" He smiled at his father's vanity.

"Play to people's fantasies," his father smiled in return. "The old man wants to die in his toy Oval Office; why not humor him?"

Barron's eyes narrowed, sensing there was more to it than that. "Why here?"

"Because just like the real thing..." An alarm interrupted President Trump. He forced a few deep breaths until his blood oxygen level was back out of the caution zone. "Just like the real thing, this replica is a Sensitive Compartmented Information Facility: a SCIF, secure from eavesdropping. I have two things to tell you."

The former president took another deep breath. "First, don't let Hyatt talk you out of the exclusive covenant prohibiting them from building hotels in the boroughs of New York without our permission. It's worth as much or more than the Grand Hyatt itself."

Barron nodded, smiling indulgently at the now familiar warning.

His father lifted a palsied hand and pointed to the portrait of Andrew Jackson. "Second. Behind there. The combination is your birthday."

Barron paused thoughtfully, then strode purposefully across the Oval Office, covering the distance in a few steps. He swung the portrait aside and opened the safe as his father continued speaking. "The brown folder. Top shelf. Should have told you sooner. You need to know."

"Folder" didn't do justice to the weighty bundle of papers in an ancient wrapper. "What's in this?" Barron asked.

"The most important secret in the world," the father explained to his son. "Open it."

Barron unwound the string that closed the folder as he walked back to his father. He removed the massive stack of yellowed paper inside, sat casually upon the corner of the replica Resolute desk, and placed the empty folder beside him.

"Read the letter," President Trump coughed, "on the top."

Barron scanned the ancient paper.

"My dear nephew,

"When J. Edgar Hoover asked me to review the papers and effects of Nikola Tesla, I knew I might find technical marvels, but I never dreamed what secrets awaited me. In an old chest, I found a pair of manuscripts, one written by the famous inventor, another by a self-proclaimed 'cowboy' Pinkerton detective named Charlie Siringo.

"In 1892, Grover Cleveland—then running for his second term as President—was approached by a secretive religious group: the Ordo Alberti, or the Order of Saint Albertus Magnus, patron saint of the sciences. They were concerned that a plot was afoot.

"James Clerk Maxwell—the famous electromagnetic physicist—died of a peculiar stomach ailment in 1879. 1888 was the 'Year of the Three Emperors:' Emperor Wilhelm I, King of Prussia died. His son, Frederick III, ruled for only 99 days, before dying in turn of a strange throat cancer. Kaiser Wilhelm II ascended to the throne. Then, Rudolf, Crown Prince of Austria, died in an apparent suicide pact with his mistress in 1889.

"The Albertians were convinced that someone was deliberately killing great scientists and benevolent rulers, retarding the progress of science and destabilizing the great powers of Europe. And now, Heinrich Hertz, the discoverer of radio waves, was seriously ill with yet another peculiar throat cancer.

"The Albertians convinced Grover Cleveland to dispatch Tesla and Siringo to Europe to take a closer look, under the cover of Tesla's lecture tour.

"The two investigators confirmed Hertz had been poisoned by a strange then-unknown radioactive substance. They were too late to save Hertz, who lingered on before a painful death in January 1893. And the conspirators killed Tesla's mother. Outraged, Tesla and his cowboy detective partner tracked down the Cabal's headquarters in Devon, England and dealt it a devastating blow.

"Returning in triumph to America, they discovered that Grover Cleveland, too, had been similarly poisoned. Only Tesla's quick thinking, Siringo's quick action, and a skilled surgeon were able to save then President Cleveland's life from the insidious assassination attempt.

"Tesla and the cowboy detective fought a long battle against the Cabal over the course of the next two decades. Finally, in 1910, they cornered the conspirators on Jekyll Island off the coast of Georgia, where they were plotting to take over the American economy through the creation of the

Federal Reserve System. They destroyed the conspiracy's evil mastermind and wiped out its lair.

"But it was too late, for the conspiracy's plans were already too far advanced. J.P. Morgan lured his banking rivals opposed to the Federal Reserve on board the Titanic. Morgan cancelled his ticket at the last minute. Jacob Astor, Isidor Strauss, and Benjamin Guggenheim went down when the great ship sank in 1912. The Federal Reserve came to fruition in 1913, and a year later, darkness engulfed Europe as war seized the continent. The course of human history was forever altered. The old order was destroyed and the world lurched toward totalitarian ideologies bent on dominating not only their own nations, but the world at large.

"I am convinced the enemy Tesla and Siringo thought they defeated somehow survived and continues to operate in the shadows, directing events and guiding actions. His ultimate ends are unknown, but he aims toward a central global government with himself as the ultimate power.

"I am not the man to stop him. Perhaps you are. I regret the only legacy I have to leave you is the burden of this knowledge. Read these notes well. Learn from Tesla's and Siringo's triumphs—and their failures.

"You must succeed at this. Or the world will fall into the endless night of tyranny.

"Your loving uncle,

"John"

Overwhelmed by the implications of his great-uncle John's legacy, Barron looked up at his father.

"It's true," his father confirmed. "Your Great-Uncle John. Very smart guy, very brainy. My father helped him go to college, get his PhD in physics. Worked on magnetrons, radar, high-voltage stuff. They wanted him to design a death ray, but he wouldn't touch it. He was one of the country's great scientists, the man tasked with reviewing Tesla's work. He gave me all of Tesla's and Siringo's notes. I studied them. You can put the originals away. I'll give you a clean copy. You need to read the whole thing."

Barron carefully slid the thick stack of papers back in the folder and resealed it.

"You know what I did?" his father asked rhetorically. "I did us all a big favor. I spent half my life infiltrating the bastard's organization. And then I smashed it." A flash of the President's old fire came to the surface. "I beat it. I crushed the bastard and caught all its helpers."

Its? One of those weird pronoun things from his youth that had dropped out of style almost as fast as it had been pushed to prominence? Barron thought back to his father's long, arduous, but ultimately triumphant struggle against the "deep state," the loose cabal of government bureaucrats who had defied the president and the people and who stole the 2020 election. "Whose organization?" Barron asked. "The rogue intelligence and law enforcement agencies? The foundations? The bankers? The globalists? The CCP?"

Who did his father mean?

"No," President Trump's attempt to shake his head was more of a quiver. "The guy behind them all. The guy pulling the strings of the bastards who only thought they were the ones pulling the strings."

Barron was still confused, but if there was one thing his father had taught him about negotiation, it was the power of silence. Keep quiet and let the other guy feel the pressure to fill the void with his own disclosures.

President Trump smiled approvingly. "Ever stop to consider what an alien invasion would look like?"

"Giant spaceships fill the skies and wipe us out?" Barron asked in jest. The intense and deadly serious look on his father's face unnerved him.

"No." There was that disturbing quiver again. "Too tough. Too far. Too hard to get here. They wouldn't send us a fleet." The President fixed his son's eyes with the intensity of his purpose. "They sent a probe. At least one. Maybe more. We're not sure."

"A probe?" Barron looked away, processing the thought. "Like a space probe? Orbiting the planet and studying us? Or like one of those Martian rover robots?"

"More like the robots," the President confirmed, "but not a go-cart with sensors. It looked like us. Could pass as one of us. Could walk among us. Its mission wasn't to take data and study us. Its mission was to guide us, to manipulate us, to control us. It tried to change our past, control our present, and rule our future"

"How?" Barron asked.

"By walking among us," his father reiterated. "By teaching, leading, luring, seducing us with secret knowledge and dreams of power and conquest. It used us as a means to its own ends."

The president paused, taking some deep breaths to collect his thoughts and keep his pulse oxygen levels up. "It showed up in China maybe thousands of years ago. Thought by ruling China it could rule the world. But its helpers saw through it, rebelled against it, and carried on a secret war against it for hundreds of years."

"The people behind the New Federal State of China?" Barron asked.

"Not exactly," his father clarified. "One of the Tongs, behind the scenes, providing intelligence and support." He gestured at the tacky Mar-a-Lago tumbler beside his bed. Barron offered it to his father.

"The Tong rebelled against their alien master," President Trump continued, refreshed by a sip of water. "Before it could build another organization, European contact happened. The Chinese were hopelessly outclassed. Getting their butts kicked. It…it moved west. Set up bases in England and America to recapture control. Tesla and the cowboy detective fought back, but the historical forces it set in motion were too great to counter. It came close, so close, to taking over our world. But we stopped it. We stopped it cold. It and all its helpers."

"What was it after?" Barron asked. "What did it want?"

"The parable of the elephant and the blind men." The president cleared his throat. "Remember?"

Barron nodded. "One felt the trunk, thought it was a snake. One, the leg, thought it was a tree trunk. One the side, thought it was a wall. One…"

"Exactly," his father interrupted him. "Aspects of the truth. The Albertians, they thought it was a demon or perhaps even Satan incarnate come to offer its followers the kingdoms of the Earth. The Chinese Tong thought it was a god called Xueshu Quan: Academic Circle or some such. The ancient teacher and deceiver. The English called it 'Springheeled Jack.' They were all right, in their own way."

The president gestured to Barron to replace the papers in the safe.

"The scientists say it's like a new kind of lifeform," his father continued. "It infects entire worlds, takes over their civilizations, and makes those worlds produce more copies of itself to infect other worlds in turn. It would have taken over. Centralized power. Unite humanity under the rule of a global government. In a few generations, it would have focused all our energy and industry into sending replicas of itself to take over other worlds. A virus. But on a civilizational…planetary scale. Exhausting us and the resources of our planet until our world collapsed."

"And you ended it." Barron was beginning to understand what was going on.

"Yes," his father acknowledged, "but I wasn't the first. I had help. There are many worlds. Right here at home. Just next door to ours. Worlds where Gore beat Bush. Worlds where the China Virus was a plague of zombies instead. Worlds where the showdown came sooner and the good guys won. Others where the good guys lost. Alternate realities. The good guys…"

The pulse ox alarm went off. The president breathed deeply and deliberately until it reset.

"One thing we had working for us. A big thing," the president explained. "The good guys figured it out first. How to cross the timeline barrier. How to reach out and share how they beat their own tyrant and his helpers."

"They were…Q?" Barron asked.

"No," the president's head could barely manage a quiver now. "They founded a different group they called the 'Reactance.' They took down the Cabal on their own timeline years before I took up the fight here. Since then, they've been contacting friends on other timelines, sharing what they know, helping them fight and triumph over their own Cabals."

Barron nodded, finally beginning to understand how so many long shots and improbable events could have played into his father's favor.

"Q," President Trump snorted. "They never did figure it out. 'Q-cleared patriot,' they said. Nonsense. That's a Department of Energy thing. Not DoD."

Barron looked back at him. "If these cross-timeline folks aren't Q, who is?"

"Our own patriots," his father explained. "In their timeline, the patriots wanted to call themselves the Resistance. Dumb name. Clichéd. The Reactance suggested the patriots join them. But the patriots were adamant they would not pick 'Reactance' over 'Resistance.' They compromised and the patriots agreed to call themselves 'Q' instead.

Barron looked puzzled.

"Reactance over resistance," his father smiled. "That's a special thing physicists and electrical engineers call the 'quality factor' or 'Q.' The name is…a physics joke. Uncle John would have been proud."

"So they set up a Q conspiracy to enlist military intelligence and right-minded patriots in every timeline they assist," Barron began to see the final layer of the "Plan" that had remained a hidden truth for so long.

Uncle John's legacy was now Barron's. "My story is almost over," President Trump told his son. "Yours is just beginning." He gestured past Barron to the big red button on the replica Resolute desk. "Push the button," the President commanded.

Barron smiled at the memory of how his father would lead on visitors to the Oval Office to think the impressive button unleashed a nuclear holocaust only to discover it summoned a staffer with refreshments. Barron turned, reached over, and pushed the button.

The side door to the Oval Office opened. A man entered.

"Hello, Barron," the man reached out his hand. "My name is Peter Burdell of the Reactance, and I'm from a timeline adjacent to yours."

"Peter," Barron gave Peter a firm grip in return.

"The bad guys have started trouble," Peter explained to Barron. "They stole some of our technology. They've begun probing across the timeline barrier, trying to infiltrate, to subvert the timelines we thought we'd cleared of their influence."

"We helped your father," Peter fixed Barron in his gaze. "Now we need your help. To stop them cold before they come back here to try again."

Barron considered the revelations he'd heard.

"Tell me more," he replied to Peter.

His father smiled, and closed his eyes.

TRUMP: REAL-ESTATE TYCOON, PRESIDENT, MEDIA MOGUL?

by Robert Ethan

Donald J. Trump.

The mere mention of his name is sure to produce a reaction of pure disgust and hatred as being a racist, sexist, despot, or a strong admiration as the great populist leader, crusading against the spread of globalism into America. Regardless of your view towards Trump, few can deny his presidency and legacy are truly unique, and there is no doubt that Trump goes against the tradition of American presidents going "quietly into that good night." Figures like George W. Bush, the previous Republican president, represent the traditional establishment and precedent of how the commander-in-chief acts when out of office.

By the way, how is Bush doing? Haven't heard much about him lately, which is quite amazing considering the absolute hatred he drew while president. I remember being in grade school when the invasion of Iraq started in 2003 and the quagmire that followed during the occupation. Each afternoon, coming home from school and right before dinner, there would be ABC News on TV, and the smearing of Bush was a given. As well as the sly comments about his upbringing, his attempts to dodge the Vietnam War by joining the Texas Air National Guard, and the fact he was seen as a complete and utter moron. Then followed Hurricane Katrina in 2005, where apparently Bush helped break the levees and allowed New Orleans to lie in ruin for a thousand years, also combined with the news that U.S. officials were using torture on Guantanamo Bay detainees during the Global War on Terror was always lurking in the background. All this created the image of a crazed right-wing despot.

However, even with his turmoil in office, a new sense of appreciation has fallen on Bush. Even Michelle Obama is photographed hugging him, and Bush has become a part of the perceived return to normalcy, as to how Republicans should act. Yet, it doesn't take a great political observer to see Trump will not receive any similar treatment by the media, academia, Hollywood, and so on. Nor will the former First Lady Obama be wrapping her arms around him, for the simple reasons that Trump is not a part of a great political dynasty. However, it is easy to see members of his family becoming the next Kennedys. Trump has not followed D.C.'s rules, and the hatred of him is one of the things that keeps that abomination known as the Democratic Party together. I do believe after this year, 2020, Trump will not have a second term, as the powers that be have ensured Joe Biden will be the next president. So what will Trump do next, and what is in store for him? There is no chance the country's elites will leave him alone, nor will Trump let things be.

First, what will the elites do to Trump? Well, pretty much what they are doing to him right now: a media campaign to discredit him and his legacy. This will continue the Russian collusion narrative, his supposed failure on the Chinese Wuhan COVID-19 response, impeachment, and his contention of the 2020 election; big surprise there. The media will also use Trump to explain away all of the Biden administration's inevitable shortcomings, as it is easier to say Biden inherited a broken nation and system caused by Trump than to admit Biden's mistakes caused by his hack cabinet and declining health. Also, it is not out of the realm of possibility to suggest there might be an attempt, by someone looking to gain recognition or fame, to try and sue or press criminal charges against Trump over a whole host of things, like his taxes, alleged sexual harassments, past shady real-estate deals, and the suffering caused by Trump's response to Chinese COVID-19 virus. However, these attempts will gain only media attention, and nothing substantial, such as prison time or lawsuit settlements, will result from it. I mean, let's face it: the FBI and the entire U.S. alphabet soup of intelligence agencies have spent the last four years trying to dig up dirt on Trump and get him out of the office and their efforts failed. Yes, he was impeached, but like the popes and their overuse of excommunication by the time of the Reformation, it has lost its effectiveness.

Now, to Trump. One of the reasons why people love him so much is his brashness. It is difficult to imagine this will go away, especially with the question of voter fraud from this last election and Biden stealing the election. Trump will be vocal about this and is out for blood, but who will give him a platform? Twitter will certainly not, as it is currently engaged in censoring him as some of his Tweets result in people not being able to comment or like them. And you can be certain following January 20, 2021 that the blue checkmark on Trump's account will be removed. Quite possibly, Twitter will ban Trump's account altogether. So, Twitter is unreliable, along with all other social media and any mainstream news networks, with the exceptions, of course, of Fox News and OANN…well, maybe. Fox News is gaining the reputation of being fickle for not pushing the election fraud hard enough. Therefore, Trump's logical choice is to take the libertarian route and simply make his own platform and news network; as his net worth as of 2020 is $2.5 billion, he has the power and resources to make it happen. It is also difficult to imagine Trump will stick around New York City after his term, as the city has already rejected Trump and may be used as a battleground against him. Any weenie of a mayor or governor would love to give Trump a hard time and sideline any real estate or property ventures and crush any firm or person who dares to try to work with Trump in New York. Florida is the spot where I see Trump relocating, at Mar-a-Lago, and creating a new power base there.

With his vast resources and the ability to create a platform for himself, Trump can easily enter into the realm of cultural significance like Joe Rogan and Alex Jones or even surpass it. Like the alternative media giant, Trump mirrors Alex Jones to some extent. Jones was deplatformed and lacks any credibility among mainstream media and culture. As mentioned above, Trump will likely be removed from the majority of social media. Nevertheless, Jones commands his followers' respect, and like Trump, people either love him or hate him. Both Trump and Jones have larger than life personalities. However, Trump has something Jones doesn't: having been the president of the United States of America, and money. Alex Jones only has a net worth of $2.5 million, yet still has the counter-culture following and persona; imagine what Trump can do with his billions of dollars and legacy. This will give more weight behind Trump's message and bring in the baby boomers and MAGA people for certain and possibly become a thorn in Biden's side regardless of how short his presidency is, and maybe even be a burden to a Kamala Harris administration. I see Trump becoming the next Alex Jones in terms of how the mainstream media perceives Jones and his role in media: a whacko conspiracy theorist drawing on meme power. For Trump, he will be noted as a one-term president stuck in his conspiracy theory of election fraud, with a strong following among the alt-right and counter-culture scene. I highly doubt Trump would have to resort to selling water filters and Super Male Vitality supplements. Still, I would pay money to see the former president rip his shirt off like Hulk Hogan, yelling "Get away from me, racist!" or screaming at Piers Morgan "1776 will commence again if you try to take our firearms!"

But the question is, what message will Trump broadcast to the world, and what would the network look like? The best scenario is that Trump and his network go back to the 2016 message that got him elected in the first place, and really emphasizes the ideas of American nationalism and constructing an effective fight against globohomo. However, the 2020 message of election fraud and "trust the plan" level of content can easily be what comes out of a Trump media network. Or the absolute worst-case scenario is Jared Kushner worms his way into this like he did with the administration and weakens any America First message. And Kushner may use it to launch his own campaign, or at least Ivanka Trump's political career. Nepotism is not out of the question, either. For commercials and advertisements, get ready to see more of the My Pillow Guy and Sebastian Gorka.

Finally, as for the 2024 election, I don't see Trump running again as president due to his age and the GOP's reaction as it tries to find a new image after 2020 and move away from Trump. But Trump's 2016 message and the image will be invoked, like how modern conservatives and boomers use Ronald Reagan. This will be especially common among the Tom Cottons, Matt Gaetzs, and Josh Hawleys of the Republican Party, who will claim to be the successors of Trump's populism against the likes of Mitch McConnell and the G.I. Joe Dan Crenshaw of the Republican neocon agenda. Regardless of what does happen, Trump is not going anywhere and will still engender resentment in liberals, and it will be exciting to see an unrestrained Trump go after them.

SACRIFICE

by Sam Tidd

The skyline never quite looked the same since the fighting began. The Washington Monument no longer pierced the clouds, its bones now littering Lincoln's Pool. The Pool itself reflected nothing, now blackened by ash from the burnt trees which surrounded it. The pinnacle of the monument currently pointed towards the ruins of the Lincoln Memorial. The Great Emancipator was buried in his own temple under tons of rubble, and with him, all that remained of the country that existed only ten years ago. It was fitting, Trump thought, that the whole city now existed as a memorial for what used to be the United States of America. It deserved to die. It had failed his son, his wife, and himself most of all. His pale hands tightly clutched the ceremonial wreath as he hobbled towards the jagged white block. He felt nothing as he set the garland at the base of the repurposed monument, the once proud monolith now a tombstone honoring the countless souls who died that fateful February day. His name might as well be on that wall, he thought; he was as dead as they were. The names Melania and Barron passed before his eyes. He calmly turned around and saluted his black-clad honor guard, who in response fired their rifles to honor the dead. The pain in his leg was tremendous as he made his way towards Guardian One. The people had to see their leader standing tall. They had to know who was still in charge. Who they should fear.

As Guardian One's engines roared to life, Trump took one last look out the window. This huge mess of rubble and debris no longer held any strategic value. Still, the symbolic power it possessed was worth the lives spent to wrest it from the hands of the Chinese. As he looked through the shuttle window, he caught his own reflection staring back at him. Gaunt and bald, his sunken eyes and milk-white pallor gave the impression of a ghost. This suited him fine. As the ship ascended into orbit, Trump thought back to this same day ten years ago. He remembered it as a normal day like any other at first. For about a month, the country had remained in a state of disbelief over the mountain of evidence which had been presented to Congress. It was clear even to the Democrats they could do nothing but reinstate him. There had been no riots. That should have been his warning sign. He thought the system had worked, that wisdom and courage had prevailed. He was wrong. It had all been rigged to do more than remove him from office. It had been rigged to remove America from the global power structure. Chinese infiltrators aided by various dissidents smuggled a large supply of explosives into D.C. and detonated them. The ensuing chaos made the Chinese invasion fleet's assault on the East Coast relatively simple. He shuddered to remember that fateful night as White House personnel hastily evacuated. His wife and son were gunned down feet before making it to Marine One. They had no time to retrieve the bodies.

The ship touched down lightly inside Trump Station's hangar bay. Trump strapped on his powered leg harness and leisurely walked down the exit ramp. The harness' motor softly hummed as he made his way down cold steel corridors to his command center. As he entered the large room, he saw his son in law looking over a stack of papers at a desk situated close to Trump's own. They exchanged pleasantries and Jared gave his daily reports. The war was progressing well. The end seemed so close now after so many years of bloodshed. Not only had they pushed the Chinese off the continent, but virtually all the rebel factions had been destroyed, save but a few. Pence's Liberators only held a small portion of California, and once they were eliminated, the next phase of America's rebirth could begin. America would be greater than it ever was before, and it would be built on a foundation greater than liberty. It would be built on power. Mike had been foolish to turn his nose up at America's one chance for salvation. Trump knew how to win, and he knew that required doing whatever it took, allying with whoever it took to build a country where safety was a guarantee and treachery was repaid tenfold. Trump would show Mike how to win. He thanked Jared and dismissed him for the day. The One would be contacting him shortly.

The One's rise to power was incredible, to say the least. He appeared seemingly out of nowhere, singlehandedly brokering peace and alliances between nations that had been enemies for hundreds of years. His careful maneuvering and scheming quickly made him the de facto leader of more than two dozen nations. His skill with diplomacy was only matched by his aptitude for invention. He was a one-man Renaissance. He had singlehandedly made so many advancements in every field of science that it seemed as though 500 years of human technological development had happened in the blink of an eye. And these advancements the One happily shared with the rest of the world, causing even his harshest critics to admit he must have the good of humanity at the heart of his ambition. His restructuring of the U.N. into a governing body was hailed as the greatest step ever taken towards world peace. The One had been Trump's most vocal advocate in condemning China's senseless act of aggression towards the United States. His organization of sanctions on China as well as providing the U.S. with advanced technology singlehandedly saved Trump from total destruction. China was slowly being choked to death, with massive famines and a future revolution certain to finish the job. They had been defeated, bigly. All Trump had to do now was repay his one true ally, which he was happy to do. The holo-projector in the center of the room flickered to life as the One's image came into being. "Hello, it's been a while," the One said languidly. Trump had never seen someone so beautiful and at the same time so disturbing. He bowed reverently as he said, "Too long my friend. I know why you called. I apologize for the delay, really! They should arrive within a week, two tops!" The One smiled bemusedly as he said, "I already knew about the delay. Don't worry about it, I know you will always be grateful for all I have done for you. I thought you would like to know where that little pest of yours is hiding out." "Mike?!" Trump exclaimed. "Yes," said the One coolly. "He's hiding out in the Redwoods. If you move fast you might catch him."

The dropship touched down quickly. Soldiers rushed out hurriedly as Trump followed close behind, his footsteps compacting the dirt underneath as he moved in his huge power armor. At first, it seemed like the One had lied to him. A second later, he wished he had. Gunfire erupted from everywhere it seemed like. Men died in heaps as Trump scrambled for cover. "How did they set up so quickly?" Trump decided he'd figure that out later as he turned his plasma cannon on an unsuspecting rebel taking cover by the trunk of a gigantic redwood. The lightning blue explosion instantly incinerated the poor fool as well as a significant portion of the tree. Bullets harmlessly bounced off Trump's thickly-armored chest plate as he turned to face the incoming fire. He made short work of the remaining ambushers as the rest fled deeper into the forest. Trump gathered what remained of his men and pushed further in. He wouldn't let Mike get away; not this time. After walking at least a mile, it seemed like they had lost their trail with tracks ending abruptly at the base of tree trunks. Sensing another trap, Trump ordered his troops to fire into the canopy above. Much to his soldier's surprise, bodies started falling to the forest floor as shots were returned in kind. Trump laughed as he blasted terrified Liberators off branches like a child shooting squirrels off a tree. His fun was cut short as he heard a mechanical thudding rapidly getting closer. As he turned to face the sound, one ton of metal plowed into him, knocking him back a considerable distance from the fighting. As he picked himself up off the ground, he saw a familiar face. A little older certainly, a little more weather-beaten and sporting a gruff white beard, but it was him. He called out to him, "Mike! Where have you been, buddy, I've been looking everywhere for you!" Pence's eyes narrowed as he said, "I've been waiting here, for you. You think you can deal with the devil and not face justice?" Trump answered him smoothly, "It's just business, Mike, you wouldn't understand." Pence, trembling, shouted back in rage, "IS IT BUSINESS TO SEND THOUSANDS OF AMERICANS TO BE SACRIFICED TO A MONSTER?" Trump simply smiled.

ABECERY LESSONS, NIGHT VII

by Jim Bonner

"Lo: a man emerged from the throng; a man of great renown, of high status and wealth. And he descended from his golden chamber, mocking those on the stage who had sapped the land of its color, and saying to them: 'Why do you all, who stand before the crowd, have the stature of a field mouse yet rest in the eagle's nest? Why do you claim to be familiar with the ways of the people when you wall yourself up from them?'

"To this, they were taken aback, and they accused him of slandering the sanctity of the stage.

"But the man ignored them and said: 'Tell me: if the color of this land is sapped, where has it gone? Were you not the ones entrusted to preserve it?'

"And they slandered him again, saying: 'There were never any hues other than the two we now see. There is the light one, which we represent, and there is the dark one, which our enemies embody. Tell us: which do you belong to?'

"And the man said: 'Whichever produces these.' Then he took out a prism and held it before the Sun, and a vibrant parade of colors appeared on the stone floor. The throng that had gathered looked on in amazement, silent still, as they had been for many years.

"Then the man spoke again: 'These are the colors that have been traded away for the two you now see. But they can return again, though only if you reject these people.'

"Then those who had sapped the land of its color called out to their challenger and said: 'These colors he shows you are an illusion; they originate in the shade of our enemy! It is he who must be rejected!'

"And they accused him with shouts and pointing proclamations. The people stood, watching, and then slowly, and with little notice, they began opening their mouths and their voice manifested through the man on stage, and he rebuked those who had sapped the color from the land with the roar of the silent crowd. From this cacophony, outpoured through him, great soundwaves took shape that reverberated throughout the place and drowned the tidal discussion.

"The silence was now in those on stage around the man, and many believed they would kill him for what he had shown. Others believed he could never be silenced and that the voice he spoke with came from others."

The old man paused and the spoken story faded into the crackling fire between them all.

"And which was it, Abecery?" one of them finally asked. "What was he?"

"Was he even real?"

His gaze lifted from the fire like sparks wafting from heat to ether and met theirs. Filtering through the white bristles beneath his nose, warm air entered his lungs, and as it was exhaled, he blinked twice from leathery eyelids.

"You've asked how it ended and began, and I agreed to tell you the story as told by my grandfather, whose own grandfather was there and lived it."

"But how can a story that long recounted be true?"

"Or that the man even mattered that much regardless?"

A hooting owl in the distance diverted the attention of those on the circle's verge deeper into the Library's Garden. A grazing stag, barely visible beyond the shadows, calmly raised its head at those turning, peering near it.

Their Abecery spoke again. "There is such a thing as destiny, or purpose, but only our descendants know what it was. Our task is to optimize our choices to the best outcome by aligning them with the nature we share. Many choices we fail to realize as such until they lie behind us, affecting what lays beyond. So too should we think when considering those who came before, no matter the distance between."

One of the Onpereil hesitated at his statement, staring deeply into the drifting embers.

"…The people may have discovered the colors regardless, but it was his destiny to show them."

His Abecery agreed. "The man becomes myth so that the myth can become a man."

"How does the story continue?" one asked.

"You do not want the story! You've all wanted the man-myth process reversed, to filter out of the story what truly occurred. This reduces its value, and so there is no use in reciting the remainder."

The Onpereil around the fire hid their chided faces behind blank stares, but the hooting of the owl returned to mock them.

"Instead, I will summarize what was left of the story."

Smacking his lips again, he swallowed, furrowing his jowls.

"Some people's voices return to them and they begin speaking amongst themselves, and some shout at the usurpers on the stage and tear it down. And with pieces of the rubble, they build…myth."

He held out his arms, looking up and around, then looking back down to the Onpereil, who stood above him.

"But since you don't want that, I'll tell you about the men. Because all the turmoil your forefathers endured against were lies, simple and unreal. Since lies go against reality, eventually reality catches up and someone eventually has to pay for them."

He smacked his lips again.

"The price was paid. The passive-aggressive things only said in private were out in the open, and there were no duels to settle disagreements in those days. Things could only escalate."

Fervidly, an arm of a burning log cracked and fell off, sending a wave of sparks flickering into the stars.

"The violence in the streets, unheard of before, became a norm.

The reaction to the growing sentiment—of feigned crisis and social regulation—made it worse for those who believed. Then, after the 'man of the myth' succumbed, there was open war. Many died before they could truly react or choose. Both believed things would be clean, like the films they had seen since their infancy. Instead, they were pushed and thrown facetiously. And the first of these conflicts was not the last. What was spoken of as impossible happened again."

"So the true story didn't start until he had left it?"

"My aunt has told me it was very simple and few people were hurt."

"Everything changes, the seasons evolve. We, as people, change, but we can direct that force. The story changed because of him, the story we are still living now. The inklings of action were forming in closeted cells, here and there, but he pushed them out into the open, whether intended or not, and made them adapt or diminish."

Their Abecery gave a long inhale and exhale.

"All great shifts have a slow, long prelude of arranging the board before the game is played, long contextualization preceding a sudden shift. But this man shifted the onset's alignment by replacing pawns with knights and bishops and kings."

The distant sound of plodding steps grew closer. A figure dressed in combat-regalia emerged from the dark, entering their space and announcing his presence.

"Onpereil all, please excuse the interruption. Your Abecery has been summoned to a meeting of the Guard."

"What's happening this late?" the Abecery inquired.

"There are calls for war," the sentry said, with trepidation worrying his voice.

Their Abecery stood and his students straightened, respectfully, and nodded at him.

"All of you go back to your homes. Ask those there of their traditions and how they came to be Founding Families. And listen to their myth without interruption," he said, raising a finger.

The Onpereil bade him farewell and left the Library's Garden by the torchlit path, back into the city-hub. The sentry moved near their Abecery and held his arm for stable support. Together, they walked away from the fire, toward the Library.

"Thank you for helping me."

"It's not an issue at all, Abecery. I'm happy to help deliver you."

"No, no, I mean for separating me from them."

The sentry chuckled, perplexed, as they meandered past the hooting owl.

"Ignore me; I've lost my wits at such a late hour, like I've lost my beauty long ago," he laughed, wheezing. "I doubt I will be of much service to the Guard, like I was to the Onpereil. But if one cannot be good looking or smart, then they must be good at looking like they are smart."

The sentry silently agreed as the Abecery finished.

"I am not equipped to communicate the truth to them, even if I knew it."

THE ORANGE MARTYR

by Brick Layer Supreme

Donald Trump, as we all know, has been a polarizing figure ever since he announced he was running for POTUS back in 2015. The libs called him racist, the established GOP said he would never get nominated, and then there were folks like my family. To us, a family of immigrant, blue-collar, order enthusiasts, it seemed he fell from Heaven. He came roaring through the candidates, swatting them down like flies one by one. He said what everyone was thinking, and that was what won him the presidency. Throughout this entire process of the primaries and the campaigning and finally winning, I was one of his top guys, which is why it pains me to write of what is coming, at least my prediction. In this short essay, I will explain my predictions as to what will happen in the case of a single term presidency for Trump. Though, at the time of writing, December of 2020, there is still hope for a second term, I foresee dark days approaching. Many in the community are having troubling dreams, be it war, subversion, or survival, and I believe them to be warnings of what to expect in the coming months, maybe even years. Mysticism isn't exact, nor is it real evidence, but something I've learned from the community is that we should trust what we can't confirm, gut instincts. So, if you would so flatter me, please come along my prediction if Trump were to accept the FALSE "win" of Biden and step down January 20th.

Humiliated, Trump formally concedes his "loss" to Biden. He takes his leave quietly as the crowd of a couple thousand libs (socially distanced to seem like there's actual support for the senile old man) cheer Biden on during his inauguration. Trump looks at his phone, scrolling through

Twitter, seeing the media rail on about how his "tyranny" is finally over and we may return to normal once again, no more kung flu and a revamping of war in Syria. To us, this is a dire situation. Our dear leader reduced to a mere man with a bad addiction to tweeting. What will he do with his ambition?

This is how I see it. Trump is now the figurehead of the true "conservative" movement, whether he likes it or not. With the attacks he is receiving from "both sides" of the aisle, the desecration of his name from being synonymous with wealth and power to "muh racism and sexism," and the international NWO/banking/globalist government elites of the world, Trump really has nothing to do BUT continue pushing for a better world. Imagine if anyone else had this same thing happen to them, or even on a much smaller scale: lies about you and your family spread, your livelihood is taken from you, your life is threatened daily. What would you do? You have been backed into a corner; all you can do is go on the offensive at that point, survive. How can he get a loan when the banks claim he is too racist for one? What city official will permit him to build new hotels? He most likely will not even be allowed to be recognized as a former POTUS, shunned from future inaugurations or those fun little promo pics of former presidents donating blood or whatever. The system has poisoned the view of one man to the point that he cannot even function as a normal citizen after being a public servant, which is something I fear will follow quickly after he leaves for all of us (the being a normal citizen with your own thoughts).

We know how Big Tech (Facebook, Twitter, Google) was able to get away with shunning Alex Jones off the Internet, a supposed "radical" that any decent person would want shunned from public life, so we can just assume that the trend will continue into all areas of life for all. Trump will be the Alex Jones to public life, public institutions, and regularity. We all understand how the public are introduced and eventually accepting of new ideas, being the op-eds or narratives produced by the journos the elites have in their hands. They aren't the pieces that are like the clickbait "we need more trans people of indigenous ancestry" or whatever that the bugmen get off on; those pieces are distractions for the opposition (MAGA boomers and Q fanatics) and ways for the elites to cause even more self-flagellation amongst those they already have controlled. How humiliating t must be to be a male feminist. The pieces in the news that cause the :rue narrative come from the likes of the *MIT Technology Review,* using :he perversion of science for their nefarious goals. They introduce these deas as "studies," such as "climate crisis will cause millions to starve and mmigrate thanks to America's pollution." We all know that's a load of ıorseshit, but these publications have pushed it to the point that it went from theory to fact in the last 30 years, starting well before my time on Earth (thanks, Gore). So, with that little explanation tangent, I will go back :o my point.

The public, being bugmen who control the institutions, have all ɔeen programmed, through these articles (or newscasts) to accept "anti- insert whatever '-ism' you like]" measures by the institutions to ensure ı "safer, better" world. What better way is there to start this new age experiment then with the "triumphant" rise of Biden and Harris? What s going to stop the banks from locking Trump out of his savings? Freeze ıis cards? Who's going to care when he goes to hospital and the nurse slips him slightly more painkillers than is prescribed and he goes? The ɔugmen and feminists still think themselves somehow revolutionaries, ɔeing more fanatical than most of the bodybuilders or wignats for their respective ideologies. When genetic freaks get the chance to be "bigger :han themselves," they are going to take it. Again, now that Trump has assumed his role as the leader of the America First movement, the bugman nstitutions, feminists, and so on will use their combined might and focus ɔn delegitimizing everything he does and has done and will cut him from ıormal life. I am thinking he's going to end up in Russia because it's the ɔnly nation that respects him and his business, which will only kick off :he whole "Russia collusion" crap again. Historians will demonize him, whatever vestiges of art that is left in the West will lambast him or outright call for his execution (sickos), and he will just become another reason for :he sciences to call for less "toxic masculinity." If he tries to do the normal :hing and retire, maybe start another charity fund or two, I do not see any situation that is winning for Trump. It is only a matter of time until he is finally put down, or his family "pays the price of what he did" (seeing how :he ethnonarcissists claim that we must pay for our "ancestors' crimes," I do not see why it would not apply here).

Now, this all is hypothetical predictions for a situation in which

Trump does not push back, but does that really sound like him? I say no. Now, I will reiterate, Trump is now the new figurehead of "conservatism," or rather the beginning of the new movement. He is not a foolish man, and since true patriots have called for him to start his own news network or paper, I believe he will attempt to do just that. When making this network, we can expect it to be "canceled" upon its creation and will be relegated to the odd corners of the Internet, like *Infowars*. Trump, again, will be first major public figure to have this "perfectly okay" banishment. *Trump News* will go on to publish what is really happening, or at least to "combat" the fake news narratives that are out there. I know that Alex Jones wishes to retire soon, and really, the man should take some "me-time," maybe lose some weight and stop drinking as much, too, but we all know that guy is hell-bent on making change. I believe with this entrance into the information war, joined with Alex Jones, Trump will assume his position as the "figurehead" of the America First movement. Though as good as it may sound that he does this, it will not be enough. His "leadership" will not be enough to cause the pot to boil over.

Trump lacks the tact to call upon the boomers to do anything of use and will instead waste away at the peak, losing his opportunity to change the course of history. No, Trump will, at worst, keep the pot simmering. Trump's most important role in the next ten to fifteen years is his, let me say, "artificial martyr" status (meaning he is still alive and all, but we can point to him and say "look what he has lost for our cause!"), and I believe that with that influence, his "sacrifices," he will leave a lasting impact on America First. The man who had it all and threw it away to fight for us! "How honorable!" they will say. Resulting from this, we have two paths in my mind:

1. Biden dies real quick or is booted for the corruption the government suddenly cares about and the Harris presidency becomes a neolib's wet dream factory for pumping out grotesque ideological executive orders and foreign policy (maybe even have a federal building construction collapse once or twice thanks to Affirmative Action hiring of architects & engineers, ha ha) and we see basically the end of a free United States, or...
2. Trump's martyr status, coupled with his "underground" media company and the likes of the MAGA boomers and Q folks being

finally awoken to the reality we face, go about doing something to seriously put an end to the corruption of the world. In the case of scenario number two, I would hope at that point that the likes of BAP or Loki (or whomever forgive me for forgetting great frogs) would step in and help guide destiny towards our triumph over evil and ugliness. Trump is not capable of leading by himself, but he will be the cause of much change once he leaves office.

To summarize, I foresee, in the case of a single term presidency for Trump, he leaves office not disheartened, but willing to push back against those who wronged him, funds and produces a new media company, is subsequently banned from the Internet, and will be the test dummy for how far the NWO institutions can cut a man off from the necessities because he is "a bad man," and we either see total consolidation of the enemy's power or the creation of a strong movement made up of the unlikely (MAGA boomers and QAnon folk). Please reach out to me if you wish to discuss what I wrote; surely I missed something. I ask that you be safe and healthy, God bless.

ALL I WANT FOR CHRISTMAS IS A TWO-TERM TRUMP

by Teleolojic Jones

All I want for Christmas is a two-term Trump.

Well, and to go to midnight mass, 'tis nearly as mysterious as the incarnation itself that these two events be inexorably linked. But here we are: since the Church shepherds won't open the houses of worship, maybe Trump will. Though sadly not in time to fulfill my Christmas wish this year. How could they complain if he did force them to open our churches, these simpering pastors; they let the state authority shut the doors and felt no shame, accommodating this great evil as noble virtue. Though we can't assume it is just obedience to authority that is the virtue here. Imagine the shame in being made to tend to your own flock as God intended by that bad, bad Orange Man. This is a time of judgement, though, a time of lines being drawn, and a time for stepping over them with courage.

Considering all the despicable cowardice in courts and such in failing to defend a fair electoral process, what if Trump just doesn't leave the White House and simply carries on being President? You know, in the way the left is fond of "making things real by doing them as if it were inevitable." Imagine this: Joe Biden sets up shop somewhere else, from some basement bunker in a D.C. brownstone, say, feebly claiming victory still and trying to establish political connections, but Trump keeps the keys to the kingdom, continues on in the confidence of his legitimate victory. This would be the ultimate judo move in Bernaysian "perception management," as this seems to be all that remains at the ass end of modernity. Truth means nothing; data is collated by power, not reason, standards of logic, or moral precepts. Not at least under the cult of the children of the revolution.

We have lived in such a crazed inversion for these past few decades, where the least potent or capable have managed by nattering will to "occupy" every cultural space. And we let them. We receded because they claimed to own the right to secular spaces. We thought that at least we have our churches, our homes, our private businesses, but that has all changed now. Right-thinking people know that we have no power outside of some kind of basis in reality; we actually think that our ideas should be connected to some old fashioned metaphysical notion called "the truth." This has been a weakness, some have said. Without will to truth, what would we be, what would we do? We don't really believe in will to power without the front brigade of Veritas.

Well, now we have it. Trump has it. He did win that election; he clipped those lying scumbags at the knee. Well, the people did; they are the ones that did the voting. He won't be stealing anything if he just stays put and assumes what should have been granted to him and those who voted for him. Trump won the damn thing and, quite truthfully, "like, by a lot." Process be hanged at this point, let's all just act like he won, that the American people, a bigger than average majority, voted for the man because they are sick of this leftist crap. They want real lives with honest interactions again. The real authenticity the university Marxists are so fond of nattering on and on about. Not the authenticity of personal preference, but the authenticity of the truth in a healthy, free, and functioning community.

Perhaps this is the watershed moment we have been looking for, the moment our enemies have finally proven themselves to be irredeemably untrustworthy in the eyes of the good-hearted regular majority. It is a hard lesson for honest folk to learn, that playing fair with some people is like a child playing dress-up with a rabid dog. Best of all, we don't have to give up our principles if Trump and all of us just assume the validity of his win. We don't have to lie or compromise, to corrupt ourselves as those who are trying to steal Trump's victory have done and always do. We, under the banner of Papa T., just have to act like what we know to be true is true. Don't debate, don't even try. Just smile with pity and carry on as if things couldn't be another way. And how could they be? This is an honest statement of truth as power.

Even so, come, Lord Jesus.

SUCCESSIO IMPERATORUM

by Karl Dahl

"Barron, how do our legions fare?" asks Duly-Elected President Eternal Donald Trump from his War Throne, the oxygen tube in his right nostril noticeably flattening the natural timbre of his voice. The normal-sized nickel boron gauntlets of his most subtle power armor, navy blue with tasteful gold and red accents, tensely grip the gleaming marble fasces of the throne's armrests. "The assault on the City of London should be underway, am I right? Or was that yesterday?"

Barron Trump, entering the chamber clad in the uniform of his elite Qtorian Guard, kneels, causing the titanium tip of his flamberge smallsword's scabbard to scrape the scarlet carpet looted from Beijing's Forbidden City. He stands to his full seven foot, eight inch height, saluting his father with a clenched fist over his heart. His powerful features and stern expression are those of a conqueror. "Father, the assault is complete and the City of London is secured, with minimal damage to the historic buildings, as you requested. I inspected the zone myself this afternoon to verify completion of the mission and the razing of the structures you ordered removed; I just flew in on the Ramjet."

President Eternal Trump raises a blonde eyebrow, a playful energy on his face. "That thing is tremendous, just great. How did you do it, then? There was so much great architecture in the City, some of the best historical English buildings. My only concern about this whole thing. How does one drop that Tower of Babel glass and steel abomination without harming anything else? King's College, the Tower, London Bridge; they're right there."

Barron nods cooly. "Most of the anti-personnel and data extraction work was performed with drone swarms and small teams of Qmmandos. We then employed directed sonic weapons and the Tower Seven Solution." He swipes his hands together twice. "Nice and clean."

"The most pressing concern, Barron: what of the libtards?" President Eternal Trump glances about, slightly confused, before his eyes land on the low Corinthian plinth to his left, made from the ground and compressed skulls of his enemies after the Last Election, and particularly what lies atop it. He carefully selects the Big Mac with his gauntlet, then takes a bite.

"Father, I am happy to report that 8,432 libtards were owned bigly in Operation Twelve Ninety." Barron smugly grins. "Most on your London List were successfully owned, epic style. Our video team is selecting the choicest Libtard Ownage footage for you to post on your Twitter account. A handful from the List remain unaccounted for. We discovered escape tunnels, some quite ancient, that clearly lead into the Hollow Earth. That said, at least another portal is under our control."

"That's good." President Eternal Trump rises, grunting, from his throne to stand, the servos in his power armor whirring faintly. He casually approaches Barron and raises his right hand above his own head to place it on his son's massive shoulder, steering him to the window, which looks out over North America from its geosynchronous position in low orbit. They watch in silence as the rotation of the Earth draws a veil of darkness westward across the plains states.

"Son," President Eternal Trump says, choosing his words carefully. "My son. I can look back on a life of achievement, on challenges met, competitors bested, obstacles overcome. I've accomplished more than most men in human history, but do you know what my greatest accomplishment is?"

"For my money, abolishing usury in the West and instituting a labor-based economic system, sir," Barron comments.

President Eternal Trump nods briefly. "I am proud of that, my son, but my greatest accomplishment is you, though I owe that mostly to your mother, God rest her soul." Frisson jumps between the father and son as they let the words linger a moment. "You offered the best advice during my first administration, and were always the most forward-thinking." Trump stares wistfully out the window, considering his children one after the other. The eldest, easily led and easily fooled, who lost his children, and his honor, in the divorce that followed his seduction by a skank who was raped to death by a pack of Racially-Aggrieved, Mostly-Peaceful Protesters during the Coup That Failed: Sad! The second, loyal and lovable but an unremarkable family man. His eldest daughter, the source of so much pride and so much trouble. The youngest and thus hottest daughter, happily married off to an America First loyalist militia leader and racist podcaster those many years ago. No; only Barron could match their father's grand vision and ambition. The first Libtard Drops were conducted in the midst of the Coup That Failed: Sad!, with a teenaged Barron flying Marine One in the co-pilot's seat, General Pinochet's famous cap on his head over a pair of Ray-Ban aviators. Ah, those carefree days of fun and laughter, when father and son enjoyed the last moments, and all the little emotions, of those many traitors to America and humanity. Nearly 30 years ago!

President Eternal Trump sighs. "Time goes by so fast. The stuff they have me on is great, but...well, my body may feel like it's still 68, but I grow tired, son."

Barron turns and looks down at his father, nodding reassuringly. "You're still strong like a bull, Father. It's good to see you feeling better." He reaches over and grips his father's power armor by the shoulder, shaking him in his 400-pound mech suit playfully.

President Eternal Trump nods toward a marble sofa to their left; the pair sits, Trump letting out a contented sigh as he leans back and relaxes his body, Barron removing his sword from its frog and balancing it across his thighs. "I don't feel strong, Barron, but you know what? That's okay. We're not meant to be on this world forever. I feel that I've accomplished everything I needed to accomplish, and it's time for the next generation to take over. And I'd like nothing more than for it to be you."

Barron nods, concealing his feelings of shock and foreboding. Veteran of countless battles at the head of his Qtorian Guard, he has attuned his emotions to his mind as well as his senses, thus using fear as a guide to reality, not a barrier. The Litany may have come from fiction, but its guidance has always been true, and serves as a distillation of millennia of warrior thought. How many have died by his bullet, his blade, his orders? It is never in the midst of battle that he feels fear consume him, for there is always something to do; the worst is before a battle, when much is unknown. Such is the moment he feels himself in. *Well,* he thinks, chuckling aloud, *so be it.*

"Yes, son, it is a momentous moment. Truly momentous." President Eternal Trump takes his son's massive, scarred hands in his gauntlets and holds them together, as in prayer. "And I know that the Council will agree that you are the best man for the job, as will the people. You've done such great things for them, son," he says, his voice heavy with emotion. "Such great things."

The decision made, and transition accepted, the two Trumps decide to wait until the next scheduled Council meeting, rather than alarm the people. And so, Barron Trump's succession is agreed to unanimously by the 13 other members—Barron Trump already at the head, and President Eternal Trump serving as tiebreaker, which has never happened—and that Barron's own father-in-law, the founder and commander of America's Right-Wing Deputy Sheriffs, would join the Council in his stead, though that would mean prying him away from his hilltop fortress in razed-and-rebuilt Seattle. Barron would continue to formally command the Qtorian Guard, though his Adjutant General would take a more active role in day to day operations.

The Successio Imperatorum is announced by President Eternal Trump via his Nationalized Twitter account and met with a powerful Likes-and-re-Tweets-to-comments ratio, most Reply Guys having been liquidated by Qmmandos and Right-Wing Deputy Sheriffs in the aftermath of the Coup That Failed: Sad! A Triumph is held at the Monument to America's Eradication of Pedophiles and Behaviorally-Transmitted Sexual Diseases, last seen nearly two decades ago when a cell of revanchist GOP(e) apparatchiks were found buttfucking each other in a bunker beneath Northern Virginia. A grand classical plaza with statue garden in the long-ago razed crossroads of Nebraska and Connecticut Avenues, the Successio Imperatorum has a tremendous turnout, millions upon millions of Americans attending in person and much of the remaining population viewing online; the most ever, really.

And so it was that, after 27 years of service, the last Duly-Elected President of the United States of America did, to the tears and cheers of the people, honorably abdicate the throne to his son, Maximum General

Barron Trump, Savior of the Land and the Faith.

Ave Trump! Ave America! Ave Christus Rex!

THE ADVENTURES OF DONNIE THE ORANG

by Neil Cypress

Days in the static void of quarantine

Slipping away

Time

Consciousness drifting

A shallow pit

Wading in my own isolation

My Essence being scattered

Across the ethereal void

Timelessness

Pandemonium

ESAB Fabricator 141i Multi Process Welding Systems brought to the front doors of the infected

Black Bags

Fines Levied

The head of the slain beast rolled at the feet of the revelers in the hall. The hero known as Donnie the Orang stood proud in his tattered bloodstained garb and demanded a cool ale and a teat of a shield maiden to suckle on. Cheers and praises cried out for the conquest of the Jaeger as the door of the hall burst forth. The mother of the foul beast came in the threshold to take revenge on he who had slain her child.

Crushing Condemnations

Deterioration

Obliteration

The hall shook. The mother of the beast cried bloodlust. Every man in the hall stood frozen in fear. Her eyes met Donnie's cold icy the same eyes that watched her son take his last breaths. She flung herself from in front of the door landing on top of the two men nearest her crushing them instantly.

Bespattering Gore

The crush of skull under foot

Their blood painted the walls and sprayed the witnesses nearby. The onlookers were then consumed by the gaping maw of the mother beast.

Gnashing of teeth

Grinding of bones

Squelching of flesh

Donnie still stood resolute; feet firmly planted in the same spot they were when the doors were so violently flung open; his left fist clenched so tightly in the palm of his hand he drew his own blood; instinctively his right hand reached for the hilt of the sword in the scabbard on his back; the sweat from his brow accumulated so heavily it drip onto his cheek; his face unfazed by the water droplet and the massacre taking place around him; his mind was blank, empty, devoid of all things except his instinct, he is the Greatest, the absolute best, he has been here before—his blood calls him to slay the beast that has appeared in front of him, this is a call he will heed, a call that he will not only heed but, take pleasure in it's execution, he is the lone man here capable of the task at hand and it is he who will set this beast's head next to her son's.

Slashing of his mighty blade

Rapid footsteps of the encroaching abomination

Foes trading blows amidst the field of corpses

A battle for the ages

O Donnie the Orang

O Donnie the Orang
Trumps the mother beast with bloodied fang
Hear the roars and the steel blade's clang
The most tremendous of deals you may have ever seen
His blade stayed true, and his blows were mean.
She sliced at him with claws sharp and gnashing of teeth
But he fought back with vigor and a strong arms reach
Her foul blue blood splattered upon the raging hearth
As Donnie thrust his hand into her chest with merry mirth
Ripped out her heart and devoured it all
As his cries of victory echoed amidst the hall
And so the men sang of O Donnie the Orang
O Donnie the Orang
Destroyed the evil crone
Within the oldest mead hall of stone
In the biggest landslide victory you may ever seen
Pee pee Poo Poo
Down with the elephant queen
All my friends are turning green
Pee poo poo pee
Am I going mad? I asked myself
No, I replied
I am the king on the fucking mountain
The pauper masquerading in filth and refuse
And the farmer plowing his dying fields
Dreaming of the newest John Deere 8RX 410 Four-Track Tractor
Oh I would love to be plowing fields
Planting my seed across the countryside
I firmly squeezed my Mai Sakurajima dakkimora pillow from the

anime Seishun Buta Yarou Wa Bunny Girl Senpai No Yume Wo Minai

And got cozy while I lurked on /a/, /pol/, and /x/ in that order

While I shlonked some of that gangweed

Pee pee poosciety

Formless and transient

Just a fucking mess

Why won't you fuck me Veronica?

Seriously, though

Why the fuck won't you just fucking fuck me Veronica?

I've been a good boy.

I deserve it.

Don't you want to praise me?

Give me a reward?

Didn't I do enough to deserve at least a head pat Veronica?

You can be such a fucking bitch some times

Just like your mom

And so the legend continues of our bigly hero Donnie the Orang

A true champion of champions

Free was all the mead, and even freer were the wenches!

For his actions he was given a small gift of a million gold pieces,

And a beautiful fiefdom upon which he built the greatest tower

But he was never one to rest on his laurels,

So, he used his small gift to buy property

And serfs in which to toil on his newly acquired land.

The serfs were purchased from the neighboring kingdom at what he thought was a wonderful price.

Thus beginning the great empire of Donnie the Orang

Whose hope and wanton folly shall lead him headlong into the future

Of fang and fire

Forging the sword he shall use to slay this next beast!

State Capital!

To drain the waters from the Jarls festering swamps

For he was possessed by an malevolent Gheist

And it was this ghiest that fought him tooth and bone as he took power

A sick and ghastly spectre

Forever living in the swamps of his kingdom

Long before Donnie the Orang ever had a sight for glory.

His men were mustered for a full frontal assault.

Helmets donned and swords sheathed

As they marched toward a victory they assumed was certain.

The Gheist had sent his spectres of death and decay to greet the men.

And an epic battle ensued!

The cries of men rang across the battlefield as flesh was cleaved from bone

And ectoplasm flowed along the ground like water after a downpour.

Then a mighty roar from the rear of the guard was heard

As Donnie the Orang emerged from behind the clashing of men and spectre

He removed his sword from sheath and the clouds parted

Letting the bright rays of the sun beam down onto the battlefield.

The light blinded the spectres and filled the vigor.

Soon the foe was slaughtered and the merry band of men marched on.

The wartroupe made their camp a few miles outside the swamp.

And celebrated the day's victory and their new God King with song and drink.

O Donnie the Orang
O Donnie the Orang
Trumps the mother beast with bloodied fang
Hear the roars and the steel blade's clang
The most tremendous of deals you may have ever seen
His blade stayed true, and his blows were mean.
She sliced at him with claws sharp and gnashing of teeth
But he fought back with vigor and a strong arms reach
Her foul blue blood splattered upon the raging hearth
As Donnie thrust his hand into her chest with merry mirth
Ripped out her heart and devoured it all
As his cries of victory echoed amidst the hall
And so the men sang of O Donnie the Orang
O Donnie the Orang

Pee pee poo poo
Sliding
Falling
Slow Fade
Grasping for sand
Dissipating
Dissipating
Slowly dissipating
Back into the ether

The sun never rose in the east but yet it set in the west.
Each man bore scars on their return journey.
The Gheist took half the company with him.

It seemed as if the men would all be killed. The Gheist had ambushed them under the cover of night and destroyed a quarter of the encampment before his presence was known. Out of the tents climbed groggy men just barely strapping on their armor. By the time the line was formed half the company had been slaughtered. Seeing the utter destruction that surrounded the now battlefield filled Donnie the Orang with a blinding, violent rage. Charging headlong into the Gheist Donnie the Orang cracked him the hilt of his sword as he removed it from his scabbard. The Gheist was quick. He evaded our great hero's every attack but was unable to land a blow of his own. The battle raged on causing great damage to earth around it. Donnie the Orang's men were able to gain their composure in the respite his combat with the Gheist granted them. Three lines of archers notched their flaming arrows and let them fly at the Gheist whenever he broke combat and peppered him with holes. Ectoplasm leaked out of every wound as the creature screamed with pain. Seeing the fleeting opportunity the great warrior seized it! He swung his large claymore at the head of the Ghiest and severed clean from his body with one stroke. It bounced and rolled beside him before fading off into the wind.

O Donnie the Orang

O Donnie the Orang

Slayer of monster and gheist

Ruler over the largest fief

The greatest champion to ever wield a sword

Commanding the respect of every king and lord

The light of men and women alike

Protecting the weak with his great might

And out he peers into the world from on top of his tower

Holding the safety of his people under the wing of his power

And so the men sang of O Donnie the Orang

O Donnie the Orang

Pee pee poo poo

CONVICTION

by Peter Paradise

"Oh this is going to be EASY," Scott Hill, the Warden of D.C. Central Detention Facility, declared to the mysterious man standing in front of his desk.

"My people will be glad that you're so enthusiastic about our offer," the man said with a dark amusement.

"How can't I be? When you first came in, I honestly thought you were going to fire me for all the bad press of me allegedly turning D.C. Jail into a 'violent, gang-ridden hellhole.' Instead, it looks like I'm going to retire early with a million-dollar check, and all I need to do is look the other way while an inmate gets offed? Too easy!"

"We like to think that it is an easy arrangement, Warden."

"So what's the plan? Are you guys going to Epstein him? Send in one of your guys and make it look like a suicide? People kill themselves here all the time," the warden added helpfully.

"We're taking a different approach. The Epstein incident wound up being too obvious. People are expecting a 'suicide' now. We need something different. It's safe to say, Warden, that there aren't a lot of Republicans in your prison?"

"Ha! The inmates are over 90 percent black and from a city where 95 percent of people voted against Trump. Ain't no MAGA in my cell blocks! Only time you'll be seeing red headgear is when a Blood smuggles in a red do-rag."

"Perfect. We prefer that these events play out organically, so our hands are clean. Where are you placing him?"

"Cell Block Six. The entire cell block is made up of Bloods and Crips. It's a goddamn warzone over there. Trust me, he'll be shivved by so many brothers that he won't make it to his bail hearing in three days," the warden chuckled.

"Good. Don't disappoint us," the man spoke menacingly as he got up and left the room. The warden sat at his desk for a minute, fantasizing about the early retirement that was within his grasp. This would unfortunately result in some intense media coverage, but that wouldn't matter in a week when he was relaxing on a beach in Mexico.

He pressed the intercom to Reception. "Chantell? Has the new inmate arrived?"

"Mr. Hill! He's here. Oh, Lord, you'll never believe who it is. It's—"

***

"Donald John Trump!" Warden Hill shouted from the balcony of the second floor of Cell Block Six down to the inmates who sat at cafeteria tables in the common area of the ground floor. Bloods sat on one side of the cell block around their tables, Crips on the other.

Scientific Jasper, the leader of the D.C. Jail Bloods, turned to his lieutenants sitting around him and laughed. "Someone named this nigga after the President," Scientific laughed. His smile faded as he looked up and caught a glimpse of the prisoner as he walked in.

It was the real Donald Trump. Standing at six foot three with his mane of blonde hair, the ex-president looked over inmates of the cell block like a lion surveying the animals around a watering hole. His gaze shifted between the Bloods and the Crips. Scientific Jasper had the feeling that the President already sensed the dynamics of the cellblock.

Trump waved at the inmates and began his descent down the staircase as the warden read out his charges. "Trespassing, impersonating an elected official, resisting arrest, assaulting an officer of the peace…" Donald strolled down the stairs with a huge shit-eating grin on his face. He flashed a double thumbs up to the dumbfounded gang members. Despite being in an orange prison jumpsuit, Trump walked purposefully, as if he wanted to be here. "...treason," Warden Hill finished his recital of the rap sheet, letting the final charge hover over the crowd.

Trump got to the bottom step and comedically rolled his eyes. "Wrong!" he shouted so the warden could hear him. Donald looked at the Crips seated at the left side of the common area, and then turned to the Bloods sitting on the right. The President spotted a table in the middle of the Bloods with an open seat. Without any self-doubt, Donald strode over to the table of hardened gang members and sat down in between two massive inmates with face tattoos.

Scientific Jasper was stunned. This was Blood territory. If you weren't a Blood, you didn't get to sit at no Blood tables. If you came to his cell block unaffiliated, you were supposed to be left standing in no man's land, left to the mercy of red and blue hyenas. Yet his soldiers didn't stand up and throw him out of his seat. They were in awe of the president's presence. When you're a star, they let you do it.

The Blood's leader looked over at the Crips. They were watching. Their eyes darted from Trump to Jasper, seeing what the gang leader would do. Was he going to get violent in front of the warden, or was he going to punk out and let this transgression lie? The Bloods at Trump's table were shaking his hand and making jokes. They seemed to like him.

I'll let this slide today, Jasper thought. He would order the Bloods to get Trump tomorrow. He was in control, and he was not going to let some outsider come from out of nowhere and disrupt the system he had built. Jasper saw the warden looking down on him. The warden gave him a nod. Jasper nodded back. Permission was granted.

***

At dinner the following night, Scientific Jasper took his evening report from his lieutenants. Despite being one of the largest and wealthiest gangs in the prison, he continued to receive reports of people testing them. A Blood got raped in the communal shower they shared with the cell blocks four and five. The economy was getting tougher. The Chinese Triad gang in Cell Block Three was flooding the market with counterfeit cigarettes, manipulating the prison currency market. Lastly, a report came from Cell Block Four. There, a few cells worth of Bloods found themselves in a cell block dominated by the Nation of Islam, and tensions between the groups ran high.

After receiving all the bad news, it was time for Jasper to issue orders and retake the initiative. "Kordell," he turned to his second-in-command, "where is the new inmate?"

"You mean President Trump? He in his cell cleaning. One of the homeboys gave him a tour of the yard and showers, so he learning his way," Kordell reported.

"Well, Donny ain't no homeboy, so stop treating him as such," Jasper rebuked. "He fucked up, coming in here and sitting at one of our tables. That's Blood territory. All them Crips, they see that. They see that, and hear about one of our real homeboys getting turned out in the showers, and they start thinking we weak," Jasper said sharply, chastising his lieutenants for not comprehending the situation. "Now we still the richest, strongest motherfuckers in this house, but I won't have no Crip laughing at us. And right now, they are laughing at us for having this goofy white motherfucker sitting at a Blood table, ya feel?" Scientific Jasper was right; the Crips were laughing about the situation.

"So what do you want done?" Kordell asked.

"I want you to go to his cell with the homeboys he was sitting with. Demonstrate to them what we do to someone who enters our territory. If Donny thinks he can act like he has blood in, then show him what blood out looks like."

***

"That's trips!" Ranger Rashon shouted triumphantly, pointing at the dice. The 30-year-old ex-military Blood was not enjoying his time in prison, but the weightlifting and games of cee-lo were welcome respites from the monotony. He had spent the past 20 minutes shooting dice with a young Blood outside of Trump's cell and had finally won his opponent's final cigarette.

"Man, this game is bullshit," the youngster said, reluctantly handing over the cigarette.

"Alea iacta est: the die has been cast, son!" Rashon took the cigarette, reciting the motto of the company he used to serve in. Rashon was about to continue teasing his opponent when he noticed something. Bloods were slinking away from the common area. Something was about to go down.

Rashon got up and began to scurry off to his cell. Whatever was about to happen, he didn't want no part of. As he passed Trump's cell door, a feeling of obligation hit him. He had to give the newbie a heads up.

Rashon poked his head into the president's cell. Trump was inside mopping the floor. The billionaire hadn't mopped a floor in decades, but he was so disgusted by the condition of his cell that he wasn't going to accept the situation. "Yo, uh, Mr. President, something is about to go down. So watch out," Rashon warned, feeling awkward talking to his former commander-in-chief. Trump gave Rashon an appreciative nod and resumed mopping.

As Rashon hustled back to his cell, he saw Kordell approaching his direction, followed by a mob of Bloods. They were descending on Trump's prison cell. Kordell stormed into Trump's cell and stood in the doorway, trapping him in.

"Hey, Donny! You think you can park yo' ass in Blood territory and it gonna be okay?"

Trump didn't seem fazed. Rather, he seemed amused. "Oh you're a tough guy, Kordell, real tough," Donald nodded sarcastically as he continued to mop.

"The fuck you say to me, bitch nigga?" Kordell shouted at President Trump.

"Kordell, shhhh, I'm mopping," Trump held up a finger to his lips as he hushed the Blood's second-in-command.

"I'm going to poke your white ass full of holes, old man," Kordell said as he whipped out his shiv and lunged towards Donald. The Blood's foot landed in a thick puddle of liquid soap that Donald had set seconds before the gang leader arrived. Kordell's foot slipped under him, causing him to trip onto the ground.

"Aw, shit, it getting real up in here!" one of the homeboys shouted as Donald Trump grabbed his mop with both hands and proceeded to batter Kordell's neck with it, as if he was swinging a nine iron. WHACK! WHACK! WHACK! Trump kept golf-swinging the mop against the Blood's neck until the handle shattered. Without hesitation, Trump gripped the sharp, splintered shard of the wooden handle and began to stab Kordell in the chest, like he was killing a vampire. The mob winced as blood splattered from each time Donald stabbed the dying man. Kordell tried to gurgle something, but a final stab from Donald silenced him.

"Fuck around and bad things happen, Kordell," Trump spat before looking up at his shocked audience. "How about that swing, folks? Big beautiful swing...people say to me all the time how I'm a tremendous golfer. And that shanking! I don't think anyone's been shanked like that in this prison, maybe ever," Donald said as he got up and headed over to his sink to wash the blood off his hands. The President was disgusted by the blood and began to take off his stained orange shirt. "Nasty stuff, folks, but it's got to be done. It's got to be done. Go on, get him out of here," Trump ordered the astonished crowd as they watched him undress. "No one knows killing like I do. Soleimani...Baghdadi...'tough guy' Kordell, they died like dogs."

On the other side of the cell block, Scientific Jasper watched the crowd that had formed outside Donald's cell, concerned. He couldn't see what was going on inside, but the hush that had fallen over the Bloods told him that things weren't going according to plan.

Back in the cell, Donald Trump had captured the complete and utter attention of the Bloods standing outside. They were so shocked by a septuagenarian murking their second-in-command, a Crip killer, that all they could do is stand there in dumb silence as Trump spoke. "The Bloods, we used to be the best. Unbelievable killers. Widely respected. We were run by sharks, total sharks. Now," he pointed at Kordell's bloody corpse, "we've got total losers running our gang. Losers. The rest of the prison, they're laughing at us. I've never seen anything like it. People in the yard, they come and say to me, 'those Bloods, not so strong anymore.' And they're right. We used to win, folks. And we will again. No one knows winning like Donald Trump does. Believe me, I know comebacks. You listen to me, and the Bloods will be stronger than you've ever seen in your entire life," Trump declared.

The Bloods stared at the shirtless president in silence. It was a lot to take in. He just shivved to death their second in command, essentially declared himself to be a Blood, and was...now asking the Bloods to make him one of their leaders? Was this allowed? A couple of the Bloods seemed to be buying his juice and clapped. "You gonna make the Bloods great again, Donny?" one of the gang members shouted, half-joking, half-hoping.

"We have a lot of problems, folks, a lot of problems. We aren't protecting our showers. Latin Kings from Cell Block Five come in and start raping our people, and we do nothing about it. No more. We're going to protect our showers, and we're gonna keep the Latin Kings in Cell Block Cinco. No one knows border security like I do. We're going to pack our showers with strong, tough men, and we're going to send the Latin Kings—I call them the Latin Queens—back to Cinc-ico. And they're gonna pay for it."

***

30 minutes later, Trump was standing in the communal showers, running his bruised fist under a stream of cold water, reflecting on his victory.

The Bloods had stormed the communal showers and promptly began to beat the ever-living shit out of the Latin Kings who were lurking around the room. The Latin Kings called in reinforcements, but it was too little, too late. The Bloods jumped them the moment they entered the shower. The 45th president dove into the brawl throwing punches and at one point head-butted a 19-year-old Guatemalan covered in crown tattoos. After wrestling the Latin King's leader to the ground, Trump stood over him.

"Do you know who I am?"

"¡Si Señor…lo siento…el presidente!" the battered leader trembled, eyeing the intimating Bloods that surrounded him.

"Go home to Mommy and Daddy," Trump said, releasing him. The leader began to scamper away.

The Guatemalan teen that the President head-butted stood up, his nose bleeding profusely. "Maybe I'd go home to my parents, if you didn't separate us at the border," he growled resentfully.

"Maybe I'll separate your head from your fucking body if you don't piss off," Trump muttered, causing the young gangbanger to limp off back to Cell Block Five. "And by the way, that's fake news... that was started under Obama! Who built the cages?" Trump called as the teen fled.

Trump felt a tap on his shoulder and turned around. It was Darryl, a 25-year-old Blood with gold teeth but kind eyes. He held in his hands a red do-rag. "That was the wildest shit we've seen in years. We own these showers now. Ain't no one gonna be punking our boys. President Trump, you a Blood, and the realist nigga in this here cell block. We ride with Donald Trump over here, nigga! Real nigga Donald Trump!" Darryl raised the red do-rag and placed it on the President's head, as if he was placing a crown of laurels upon a Roman general. The Bloods began to hoot and holler and then broke out into a chant.

"Real Nigga Donald Trump! Real Nigga Donald Trump! RNDT! RNDT! RNDT!"

Trump soaked in the praise. It was like the rallies, only somehow more satisfying. Looking up at the ceiling, he saw one of the security cameras in the shower pointed at him. Its green "on" light was engaged. He smiled. Trump loved being in front of a camera, and hoped the warden was watching and getting triggered.

***

Scientific Jasper stood in the prison yard with seven furious gang leaders staring daggers at him.

"You need to get your gang under control, *ese.* Your homie Trump is causing lots of problems for our business," the MS-13 leader declared accusingly.

"He ain't my homie," Scientific said defensively. "He may think he is one of my lieutenants, but just relax; tomorrow, he will have his bail hearing and then he's gonna be on the outside. My hands are tied. He's popular; if I try to murk him, the gang will turn on me. He heading out the door, anyway. Be patient, niggas!"

"It's not enough to just have Trump out of prison; we need these ideas he is spreading stamped out. They're bad for business. Trumpism has to die with him," the leader of the Chinese Triad spoke up. "The Yellow Brick Road has been disrupted, and our contacts outside aren't happy," he warned menacingly.

A Russian mafia member spoke, "It's a problem, comrades. Already people who aren't Bloods are thinking of defecting to their gang. They say Trump vill shiv all pedophiles in this prison, and that ve need to 'trust the plan.'"

"He's having them loud rallies out in the common area, and it's pissing me off!" the leader of the Crips growled.

Scientific Jasper tried to reassure the leaders. "Look. I'll talk to the motherfucker. Get him to back down. Tell him how things work around here. He's a businessman, he'll get it."

"You better," the Triad leader threatened, "or else everyone in this yard will be hunting Bloods this time tomorrow."

***

"Mr. President, come in!" Scientific Jasper greeted Donald as he welcomed the president into his cell. Jasper lived in a "ghetto penthouse," located on the second floor of the cell block. "You've only been here two days, and already you've got motherfuckers going crazy up in here."

"Well, Scientific, the other gangs, they're taking complete advantage of us, and we're not gonna let that happen,"

"Yeah, yeah, fo real…" Jasper's voice drifted as he calculated his next move. "Here, take a seat on my bunk…you want some refreshments? All them other inmates in D.C. Jail only have ramen, chips, or other prepackaged shit like that. But here in my house, we do better than that. You like fast food, right?" Scientific lifted up his pillow to reveal four Styrofoam Big Mac cases.

Trump picked up one of the cases and took out one of the burgers. "It's still warm."

"20 minutes ago, that burger was in a McDonald's on Pennsylvania Avenue. Now it's here. That's what I wanted to talk to you about."

"Burgers?"

"Ever since you had the Bloods take over the communal showers, it's upset the smuggling networks in this prison. You see, we have this smuggling route called 'the Yellow Brick Road.' It connects the outside world to all the cell blocks in this prison. Drugs, cellphones, contraband; as long as the Yellow Brick Road is open, we've got ourselves free trade. The whole route hinges on our showers, though. If people from other cell blocks can't come and go as they please through our showers, it all falls apart. So do your fellow inmates in the other cell blocks a favor and open the borders to these showers. We've got a trade deal where everyone wins... no downsides! So why fuck it all up for everyone when you gonna be out of here soon anyway?"

Trump swallowed the bite of his burger. "Do the other Bloods get Big Macs?"

Jasper laughed. "Hell no. This is a smuggling operation. It ain't no Uber Eats. This is reserved for you and me, my man. Elites at the top of the food chain. We get special benefits, and the rest of them niggas down there get to purchase fentanyl and other drugs from us."

"It doesn't seem like the Bloods are winning. I talk to people in the cell block. They say to me, Mr. President, our boys, they were getting raped in the shower and we weren't allowed to do anything about it. I've been here two days...and I fixed that. It was so easy. It only required will. Why are we letting Bloods get addicted to drugs? These are terrible things. Scientific, terrible things. We aren't protecting our people."

"Look, part of the arrangement with the warden is that I keep the peace. I can't be looking out only for Blood interests. Imagine if each prison gang only looked out for their own interests? It would be crazy! The other gang leaders, the warden, myself, we have a system. We maintain stability, limit the violence, and don't let there be no riots. The trade continues, and we all profit. Sure, sometimes a Blood or two gets raped or jumped by guys from other gangs. But guess what? Rape is part and parcel of being in a prison. What am I gonna do? Retaliate and start a gang war and risk upsetting the economy, stupid?" Scientific licked his lips and tried one more attempt at using a carrot to persuade Trump. "Look, I know my man likes the ladies. You stop securing the shower, and I can use the Yellow Brick Road to get you some fine ass pussy from the outside in here."

"The Yellow Brick Road can get people into D.C. Jail?"

"Yup."

"Then why don't we use it to get our crew out of this shithole?"

Scientific's face contorted in bewilderment. "What? Break out? Hell no."

"Why not?"

"Who would I sell to if my customers weren't here? Shit, Donny, I thought you were a businessman. The system falls apart if our consumers stop consuming."

"Scientific Jasper you are a lousy leader. You care more about the system than you do about your fellow Bloods, and quite frankly, it's disgraceful."

"Fellow Bloods? Why do you think we threaten people who aren't affiliated with a gang?" Jasper snapped. "We do it so them niggas end up joining our gangs, so we can control them. We're out here controlling the violence. Right now, we're stopping it, but we can turn it the fuck on, if we want. You better hope you get out on bail tomorrow. Because tomorrow, if Blood still be holding that shower, then all the gangs will be coming out against them. All of them! It's going to be Donald Trump and the Bloods versus the world."

"Jasper, you're a loser and you don't care about your people. I used to hire disloyal people to work with me. No more. I've learned a thing or two. Covfefe!" Trump shouted, giving the signal. At that, four Bloods who were secretly waiting outside the cell rushed in and grabbed ahold of the gang leader.

"You crazy! You crazy!" Jasper shouted as the Bloods dragged him outside and held him against the railings that overlooked the common areas.

"Scientific Jasper…you're fired," Trump declared.

At that, the Bloods flipped Jasper over and sent him hurtling to the ground. His head hit the concrete floor and made a sickening cracking sound. It was Trump's gang now.

***

The mysterious man sat in front of Warden Scott Hill irritated by the news the warden had just delivered him. "So you mean to tell me that not only has Donald Trump not been killed during his tenure in your prison, but he has become the leader of the largest gang in this prison?"

"Look, in retrospect, we should have seen it coming. That man's high energy. Business...politics…he succeeds at everything he does. It's in his blood. We should have known he was going to thrive with prison gang intrigue. That said, good news: he's making a lot of enemies."

"Oh?"

"Yeah, there is a tunnel that leads to one of the communal showers. It's called the Yellow Brick Road. The gang leaders in this prison use it to smuggle drugs and other contraband. I have a deal with them; they stop the inmates from rioting or starting big gang wars, and I look the other way. Well, Trump shut down that route, and now they are pissed. A little birdie told me that all the gangs will be coming after him tomorrow. I've got leaders asking me for permission to shiv him."

The shadowy man seemed relieved. "Do you think they will be able to get the job done?"

"I've got some pretty scary dudes in here. And all of them coming down on him? Oh, I'll make sure it's not a fair fight. We'll give them… equipment."

"Excellent. My people will talk to the judge. Get him to refuse to look at Trump's case tomorrow. That will buy us time to make sure that he remains in this facility. As further insurance, I am bringing one of my assets. We used him for a prison job in New York a couple years ago. You will provide him a CO's uniform and disable all security cameras when he is on site. Understood?"

***

A deep sense of unease had fallen over Cell Block Six. So many rumors were flying around D.C. Jail that almost everyone knew that in less than an hour, all the gangs in the prison were going to descend on the Bloods. Word was they were armed not with shivs, but with real knives. No one knew where they got them from.

Trump was pacing around the Bloods' side of the cell block, deep in thought. A troubled but determined expression was on his face. An eerie quiet echoed throughout the cell block. Ranger Rashon watched the President do a lap around the Bloods' side before deciding to go talk to him. He needed to know what the plan was. "Hey, RNDT. Everything okay? I heard the judge refused to hear your case today. That's tough."

"That's okay, Ranger Rashon. The justice system is totally corrupt. It's very sad," Trump answered. The two walked together for half a minute before Trump asked, "So why do they call you Ranger Rashon?"

"That's because I served in the 75th Ranger Regiment."

Trump's eyes lit up. "Terrific unit. Real killers in there. I sent them to kill Baghdadi."

"Yes, sir, Mr. President. I was on that mission."

Trump reached out and shook Rashon's hand. "Tremendous job. Tremendous. Rashon, what are you doing in a place like this? You seem like such a nice guy."

"They got me on gun charges, sir. There's a lot of crime in my neighborhood, so I kept a few guns…maybe a lot more than a few. Anyway, my ex snitched on me, and now I'm here. I just wanted to be left alone when I came, but after watching some unaffiliated people get fucked up, I got the message real quick. Now I'm a Blood, and you're still my boss. Funny how life works. How did they get you?"

"They stole the election from me. On Election Day, I was winning in a landslide. They stopped counting the votes in multiple states at once. They figured out how many votes they needed and then counted fraudulent ballots. They declared Joe Biden the winner, even though over 80 million Americans knew it was all fake. On Inauguration Day, Biden wasn't even going to have an inauguration in person because of the China Plague. So, I had my supporters come to the Capitol to watch me swear in for a second term. When I arrived, the FBI arrested me for trespassing, treason, and one of them made up a story that I pushed him."

"Damn. Well, you're the first guy I ever met with a treason beef in here, so that's something."

"Yeah, that's something alright," Trump said before abruptly stopping. Something captured his attention. Or, more accurately, the lack of something caught his attention. The Crip side of the common area was mostly empty. The majority of the Crips were congregating in their cells conspiratorially. "It's about to happen."

"Yo, Donny!" Darryl shouted to Trump as he sprinted across the cell block. "It's going down! The other gangs…they're attacking Bloods all across D.C. Jail, wherever they can find them! The big house is coming down on us!"

The big house is coming down. Oz. Yellow Brick Road. Suddenly, the way forward became clear for Trump. A plan formed in his mind, not out of reason, but out of instinct. "Darryl. The Crips will be on us soon. Tell our soldiers to get shivs, and tell the Bloods to stand back and stand by until the Crips come out. We need time. When they do come out, knock the crap out of them." Darryl nodded and ran to the other tables, passing the message. Donald turned to Rashon. "I think there is a tunnel out of the prison hidden somewhere in the showers. It's how they smuggle drugs in here. We're going to find it and then break all the Bloods out of here. Do you have anything sharp?"

"I've got a screwdriver back in my bunk."

"Get it, quick!"

A couple minutes later, Trump and Rashon passed the Blood sentries that guarded the showers. As they stepped into the white-tiled chamber they could hear the sounds of shouting behind them. The Crips were attacking. There wasn't much time.

"You think there is a way out of here in this place?" Rashon shouted as he began feeling the walls for loose tiles.

"Nobody knows buildings like I do. There are showers and toilets in this room. They are going to want to have access to the pipes in case there is a leak. There must be a utility tunnel entrance hidden in here."

A loud scream from the outside rose over the sound of the fighting and echoed throughout the showers. It was the scream of a dying man. The rumors about the knives were true. "Yo, RNDT, it's getting wild out there. Bloods are holding their own, but niggas are getting killed."

"Go help them! We'll be okay in here," Trump commanded as he followed the line of drains, trying to anticipate where the pipe was. He looked up at the ceiling where the security camera was. The green light wasn't on. *Strange,* he thought, *what a bad time for the cameras to fail.*

The sounds of fighting grew louder. The Crips had crossed over into Blood territory and were pushing the Bloods back towards the hallway that led to the showers. With the knives, it was an unfair fight, but the Bloods fought back as if victory was still a possibility.

"Keep looking around the showers; I'm going to see if I can find it in the lavatories," Trump called out as he hustled to the other end of the chamber.

The President threw open one of the toilet stalls. Felt for loose tiles. Nothing. Tried to see if the toilet would move. Bolted into place. He burst into the next stall. Same thing. Again. Again. Again.

More cries and roars from the outside echoed throughout the ceramic chamber. It sounded like there were more people out there than before. Gangs from other cell blocks were pouring in.

There wasn't much time.

As Trump thrust open another stall door, it dawned on him. Yellow Brick Road. It couldn't mean…

He ran out of the stall and went over to the urinals. Where to start? At the end was the tall standing urinal that didn't flush. The President ran over to the tiled urinal, gripped it by its sides, and heaved.

It shifted.

He put his full weight into pushing it again, and the urinal moved to the side, revealing a utility tunnel large enough for people to travel through. This was it. The Yellow Brick Road. Their way out of this prison.

Trump turned around to shout to Ranger Rashon to grab the others, but saw someone else standing there. A large brute of a man wearing a corrections officer's uniform faced the President. The man wasn't quite looking at him, but looking through him. Like when a wolf sees prey. The CO held a large knife flat against his leg.

"It was rigged from the start, wasn't it?" Trump said as he lifted his fists. He didn't have any weapons on him, but if he was going to go out, it would be out swinging.

"You weren't supposed to make it this far. Take comfort in the fact that you defied our expectations," the assassin said as he strode towards Trump.

Rashon ran into the bathroom, exasperated, "Mr. President, I tried all the tiles, but I couldn't find anyth—" He stopped himself seeing the man in the correction officer's uniform. The man halted upon Rashon's arrival, only a few yards from Donald. Behind Donald was the tunnel. So it was true. There was a tunnel out of here the whole time, but Scientific Jasper and the others had kept it secret.

"Inmate. Return to your cell immediately," the man barked.

"Not a real cop. Not a real order. The only authority he has is what you give him," Donald taunted, eyeing the assassin's knife.

"Inmate! I won't tell you again. Go back to your cell block now, or else," the guard ordered menacingly.

Rashon stood stunned. He could tell that the corrections officer was about to murder the President. The CO was big and had the law on his side. Rashon felt the screwdriver in his pocket brushing up against his leg. He could do something about this. But if he did, there was no going back. Ever.

"It'll never stop with me. They're not afraid of me, they're afraid of you," Trump stressed to Rashon.

"Inmate! Not another step forward." The CO was beginning to look concerned that Rashon was continuing to stand there.

A puddle of shower water was all that separated Rashon from the CO. The veteran slipped his hand in his pocket, pushed aside his pair of lucky dice, and gripped the plastic handle of his sharpened screwdriver.

Behind him was his cell block. Gray, soul-deadening, but predictable. Four more years until parole, assuming they would give it to him. In front of him, across the puddle, lay adventure and danger. Failure meant death or staying imprisoned forever. Success would bring even greater dangers, but at least he would face it as a free man.

Rashon tightened his grip and stepped over the puddle. It was time to roll the dice. It was time to fight for Trump.

A LONG DIVORCE: TRUMP AFTER THE ELECTION

by Chad Stacy

Journalists have short and often incomplete political memories. Much as Donald Trump's 2015 rise was hailed as unprecedented and rapid in its nature, in reality, he had talked about politics generally—and running for president in particular—since the 1980's. Indeed, Donald Trump began running for president long ago. In many respects, then, his official 2016 campaign was a protracted phenomenon, one that could have taken hold 16 years earlier.

As President Trump steps out of the White House, it is likely that his exit will be equally drawn out. There will be coverage, there will be Tweets, and there will be numerous conspiracy theories—among both QAnon and the Resistance—concerning the president's designs on seizing power. These will continue into Biden's second full month in office, and perhaps longer. Nothing will come of them, naturally. But where President Trump's eventual movement towards politics was explosive and exciting, the departure will be more mundane and anticlimactic.

President Trump will leave 1600 Pennsylvania Avenue a free man this January, and his exodus will be unremarkable. No matter how badly CNN, MSNBC, and suburban, wine-loving Democrats wish for an Oval Office stand-off, a failed coup, or some other West Wing-tier climax to the Trump saga, there will be no such drama. He will depart from the building and return to South Florida. That said, it is unlikely that he will attend the inauguration (inasmuch as there will be one, given the COVID fixation among liberals). What is almost certain, however, is that President Trump will comment on the disparity in crowd size, i.e., that his was larger. He will probably be right on this for the reason stated above, although BLMers, DMV people, and other urban folx make political exceptions to COVID guidelines all the time, and local officials allow them. Who knows: maybe Biden will have the highest Inauguration Day turnout ever.

It is likely that President Trump will remain with us for some time, i.e., he will remain the dynamic and engaged political voice we all know and love. It is clear that the Biden administration will publicize all its first Executive Orders overturning those of the Donald, starting with the travel ban EO from 2017. These will be the new administration's main focuses, and the reversals will likely ignite more than a few early morning tweets from President Trump, prompted by the celebratory coverage from CNN/MSNBC/NPR of such orders. His takes will sound something like this:

> *"WOW! Joe doesn't have a clue. Letting terrorists back into our Country during a pandemic and recession?! People will die. Remember, I kept you safe!" @realdonaldtrump 4:03 am EST*

His replies will be flooded with puerile COVID rejoinders and strawmen, and terrorist attacks will pick up in a few months. This type of situation will play out a few times until, perhaps around June or July, the former president's Twitter returns to its older, truer form. That is, it becomes a forum for Donald Trump to share his thoughts—his opinions on TV, takes on celebrity gossip, and views on sharks ("Sorry, folks, not a fan!"). His interest in politics will wane and the Professional GOP will be happy to see him step back, at least for the time being.

It is possible that President Trump remains disengaged throughout his retirement. After all, he is a billionaire in his 70's, a grandfather, and an avid golfer and traveler. Why would he want to continue working in politics any more than he has? He ran and won with the most dysfunctional campaign and party, was gypped the second time with a worse campaign and more useless party, and endured unending lies from the media and Dems. Let us not forget that all the while, he received sass and dissent from his supposed allies in D.C. The main point here is that it should not be discounted that Donald Trump does not need this. Now that he is out of office, one must ask: why would he want to continue with politics when he has no reason to do so? The answer is because he is

Donald Trump.

Neurotic and never one to learn his lesson, The Donald has limitless trust in his friends and support for his family and those he sees as loyal. Sadly, he also possesses an impressive capacity for ignoring the results of his actions and those of his enemies. It is almost certain that President Trump will remain involved with politics, even if he does not want to get involved. What will happen in 2022 is what happened in 2016 when he beat the odds and Clinton: he will be lied to and coopted by the worst people in Republican politics. The Beltway deficit hawks, liberal internationalists, and "reformers," i.e. Conservative Inc., will use him again.

These hacks—the Professional GOP people—will come to him, likely with his daughter Ivanka, who herself wants to run, and they will say that his legacy is on the line in the 2022 midterm elections. He must act to save all that he worked for. (What exactly he worked for will remain vague and nondescript; it would be a mistake to compare his vision with his record…that could lead to some uncomfortable questions.) Back to Trump. They will lie to him, and it will sway him, in part because his most loyal followers will not move with him to Florida. Instead, it will be Javanka, Brooke Rollins, and the Koch-adjacent crowd. They will smother him like an overbearing Jewish mother would her youngest son, which is to say completely.

Control of the House of Representatives—the most impotent element of the weakest, most irrelevant branch—hangs in the balance, they will tell him. If they can win back the House, then the country will be Great Again, and so too will be the President's signature achievements. But Republicans can only win if President Trump comes out of retirement, puts on the red hat, and endorses a cadre second-generation army lieutenants of Latino and/or Asian descent. That they are running on platforms totally divorced from (and likely opposed to) the one the president ran on two years earlier is not relevant; all that matters is winning marginal races in swing districts.

All of this, they will say, is essential if we are to MAGA. Like clockwork, President Trump will do what he did so many times in office: dutifully send out tweets in support of candidates he neither knows nor agrees with. None of these tweets will read like his, a fact that will be obvious to all. It is possible that, for the right candidate, President Trump, the WWE POTUS himself, might even make an appearance in person, but only if the crowd is large enough and he is given some amount of time, maybe 40 minutes to an hour, where he can go out there and riff about the news and what he thinks about it.

This ritual will occur several times over, and maybe more if Ivanka asks her father nicely. Outside of that, and beyond that point, it is unlikely that President Trump will engage with politics. To be sure, he will have more thoughts on the party and his possible GOP successor. Unfortunately for the Donald, he will have little input on the question of succession as he will not himself run again and will be too disengaged to police the primaries.

The sad fact is that the Trump Show is wrapping up. With a Democrat in office, unfavorable crises will vanish, CNN will begin anew its hunt for the black box of the Malaysian flight that went down in 2014, and coverage of Biden (assuming he makes it to 2022) will focus on his socks and palate. Donald Trump's commentary will necessarily focus elsewhere. If not, and assuming he gets too political, Twitter will simply remove him. One certainty is that once President Trump leaves office, his social media account will be subject to much stricter standards, and no one ought to assume his are too big to fail.

The upshot of these developments—the passage of time, the final victory of the Professional GOP over the former president, the temporary suspension of politics, and further regulation by social media platforms—is this: the media circus that started in 2015 will close up shop and return to slumber, ready to return if Donald Trump rises again to challenge the political consensus in Washington. But this he will not do. For the various and sometimes interrelated reasons set out above, President Trump is, for all intents and purposes, out of the political game, as it were.

To the extent that one can say that the use of Donald Trump's likeness and/or his social media posts by the D.C. GOP to sell Republican candidates that the Boss himself would have insinuated were gay only a few years ago can be called continued involvement, then yes, he will remain involved. But Donald Trump the 4chan avatar, the poaster boy of the #FrogRight, the crown prince of shitlords everywhere, will never do again what he did before: bully journalists, Mexicans, Republicans, and overthrow the guardians of the American regime as an insurgent, unapologetic Twitter candidate. Gamers may very well never see hemselves represented in the Oval Office again. President Trump will eave, but he will not be forgotten.

In early fall, 1806, and on the eve of battle in lands that we would now dentify as Germany, Napoleon entered the city of Jena atop a great horse. Calm, confident, and engaged in official duty, he was observed by a young nan: Georg Wilhelm Friedrich Hegel. The young man was struck by the presence of Napoleon, and it left an impression on him. Later, Hegel told a friend of the experience in a memorable letter. Famously, Hegel referred o the legendary conqueror as *Weltseele,* a phrase meaning world-soul, or eternal natural essence. A rare breed and likely the only of its kind in a given age, this figure—this specter, even—is the embodiment of a force that wills history and defines epochs.

What makes the prospect of parting with Donald Trump so unpleasant is the realization that he was an icon, a true one-off. Indeed, he was both more than a man and less than a god, a superstitious oracle and an academic, dispassionate killer of myths. In a sense, the Donald was more *Volksgeist* than *Weltseele,* more the fading spirit of an increasingly distant nation than a human representation of the permanent energy of the universe. He was unique, and we will not see another like him.

Whatever Donald Trump is, whatever he was to us, and whatever he will become to those after, he was a force—a great destructive force—and one that we all will continue to feel for decades to come. Whether he is drinking Diet Cokes by the dozen, cursing while playing golf, or tweeting in the wee hours, he will continue to shape the minds of his critics and burn in the hearts of his allies. All of this will continue even as the former president gradually disappears.

NEVER THE TWAIN

by Borzoi Boskovic

There's a journalist outside of my apartment door. He looks like he sweats a lot and that the salty beads mix in with dirt in his unkempt beard. He's fat in the face and fat in the belly and he knocks on my door with the anticipation of a child's Christmas.

"James Foust," he calls me by my real name. He speaks with authority, but I see the nervous twitch in his eye through the peephole. He strains to look back at me through the little glass, but I lean to the side and let the light through. I can hear his heavy rasping breathing through the door, like an elderly beast feeling the thrill of its final hunt. I close my eyes and listen to my pounding heart. I listen until I hear the steps move back down the hallway and I listen until all I hear is silence. I slump down and I sit with my back to the door. I feared this day for five years, but it still feels unreal.

I was Ethnoskate1488. I never had an actual show, despite all the jokes that I should start a racist skateboarding podcast (I've never skateboarded). I just sometimes showed up on other people's shows and streams, quick with a few edgy jokes and regurgitated points I cribbed from much more succinct but shyer posters. They called me Ethan for short. Podcasting was a way for me to blow off steam, and despite not having touched a microphone in five years, it's about to ruin my life.

Years ago, the only people interested in unmasking anonymous posters and podcasters were the few journalists who received NGO money and a legion of extremely online superhero film superfans who did it for free. A lot changed in the Biden and Harris administrations, and with a combination of public and private funds, the Justice League changed the game. Many people were surprised that DC Comics and Warner Media would work with an organization whose sole aim was to dox "anyone of interest" who had supported the Trump administration or helped get him elected. We weren't surprised in the least. Their full mission statement should be framed in a museum just for its brazen banality:

"The Justice League is a catalyst for racial, sexual, gender, and religious minority justice in the United States and abroad and beyond, working in partnership with communities and businesses to dismantle white supremacy, patriarchy, and all manners and forms of kyriarchy and strengthen the intersectional movement in order to advance the human rights of all people. This necessary task is impossible without a truthful audit of the fascist element of the Trump administration toward anyone of interest. This is the moral imperative toward a more perfect union, and the Justice League is proud to partner with conscious businesses and organizations committed to doing the work."

Instead of having radical liberals who weren't talking to each other because of various polyamorous and molestation dramas and the clout they wanted to horde, Justice League cut a swath through the personalities by paying for all of the information disparate actors had collected, collating it, and offering bounties for anyone who had information on personalities they wanted to know about. There was no personality, no commenter they weren't willing to put on blast, as they were flush with cash and people quickly became addicted to the flash target of the week once they figured out how to gamify the process. They easily bought out the people who at first bristled at this new competitor, as most of them found a new home in the organization. They fundamentally found no disagreement working for a quasi-corporation with the cushier lifestyle it afforded antifascists who had struggled during the previous years' intense lockdowns.

The journalist trailing me was a particularly odious example. Everyone simply called him the Blob. This was his full-time job, and he did it despite the debts it put him in and despite the money that Justice League threw at him never doing a bit of good. The devil deserves his due, however, and no matter what people said about his physique, his physiognomy, his life, he was relentless in the pursuit of his own satisfaction. He himself had been doxed and exposed multiple times, but no amount of shaming him about his hovel and filthy lifestyle ever dissuaded him from the satisfaction he got at getting people fired. I have friends who keep tabs on him and the sad, pathetic details of his life. It's never done anyone a bit of good.

I was shaken out of this reflection by the annoying sounds of my smartphone's notifications. It was across the apartment, charging. My body simmered in nervous anxiety at what could be on there, but I pushed myself up off the ground and walked over. It was not a long distance in my apartment, with the computer pushed to one side, the kitchen on the other, and my bathroom right next to the exit door I had rested against. I didn't need to look at the phone and I often planned ways of never looking at it without ever following through. After all, it could be my girlfriend, my mother, or my job needing me to do something. There were always a thousand reasons that I needed to stay plugged into the electric cloud.

I picked up my phone and started swiping out of all the garbage. Game notifications, special offers. There was an AMBER alert I paid no attention to, as it was almost certainly a custody issue. I saw a story about Trump, teasing that maybe his daughter Ivanka could run in his place and become the first legitimately elected female president of the United States. Swipe. Swipe. Swipe swipe swipe swipe swipe. I just wanted it all gone. There were three missed calls and two texts accompanying two of those calls. The first was from my uncle. No text. The other two were from a guy from the same political milieu who knew who I was, and the other was from Katie, my girlfriend. My buddy's text said "bro, call me." Katie's notification said "we need to talk."

I knew who to call first.

I went to the kitchen to fix a snack while the phone rang. Eventually, the voice of Derek, formerly Resaxotionary, came on the speaker. I chopped carrots and boiled water as he spoke.

"Hey. Sup."

"The Blob found me."

"Wow, that sucks. Do you need anything or any help?"

"I didn't answer the door. I don't know what he knows. But like I told you before, these people will need to post everything, as I'm not saying anything. I'll deny it's me even if they have audio of me saying 'I am Ethnoskate.' They get nothing."

"That's rough. Well, call me if I can do anything."

"Obviously this is not why you called me."

"Obviously this is not why I called you. Did you see the latest thing with Trump?"

My knife pressed down through the carrots, hitting the board with each slice.

"I saw something about his daughter. I don't know. It's all fake and gay and it has been for a very long time. I haven't been following it. Please tell me you aren't following it."

There was a pause. Derek replied, half-laughing, half-apologetic, "Well, who else are we supposed to support? I get that some guys are really into Hawley, but we can't split the vote."

I set the knife down. "That's not what I'm talking about."

"You mean the whole thing about Trump teasing that maybe he won't run and he'll support his daughter instead. I mean, it's a bit of a funny troll and a way to poke at how nobody really voted for Harris, but there's no way he's serious about that. Trump is going to be the guy in 2024."

"Trump is 77 now. He's looking a lot worse for wear; this can't be anything more than a grift to keep the money rolling in."

I grabbed the sliced up carrots and dropped it into the pot of boiling water.

"They're destroying his life, man; no one asks for all that pain and trouble just for a grift. And just look at who has betrayed him and the comments he made about Netanyahu and the people who have betrayed him since the last election was stolen from him. He knows the score, and he knows this is his last chance to deal with these people once and for all, otherwise it's all over for him. Guys like you just had too high expectations for him. You wanted a Hitler, and that's not what he is. But he can still do a lot of good for us, at the very least by not being one of these neoliberal shills."

"I haven't done politics since 2018 and I never asked for that. God damn—" I stopped myself before I said what I wanted to say. I wanted to say "you lost your wife and she has custody of your kid because your support and online comments led to your doxing, stop making excuses for a con man." I couldn't. I'll take whatever friends I can get these days.

"Sorry, I'm just tired of hearing stuff like that when that's just not true. You tell me what the benchmarks are for Trump to be good for the cause or the movement or whatever, and I'll point to where he's failed and failed time and time again. It's just how it is and not being President Harris isn't enough for me to care. Aren't there any groups or chats you can discuss this on?" I asked, somewhat exasperated as I tossed the block of ramen noodles into the boiling water.

"Which? Can you name me one? They're all gone, Ethan, and none of the new ones are trustworthy. I'm not discussing this with anyone who didn't go through what we went through."

Then why do you keep hoping.

"At least promise me that if for some reason Ivanka gets the nomination, you won't support her."

Another pause. This time it was longer.

"We have to buy time, and the Trump name is useful."

I didn't know what else to say anymore. I sighed and finally told him, "It was good to talk to you again, Derek."

"It was good to hear from you, Ethan. Let me know if the Blob causes you any problems. I've lost touch with a lot of the old crew, but I could see who is still around and who I can scare up."

"Thanks, bro, but I think we're all on our own now." I poured the ramen and carrots into the bowl, keeping most of the salty broth in the pot. I applied my bit of mayonnaise and bacon bits and stirred.

"Ain't that the truth."

I sat in the silence of my apartment and ate my concoction. I didn't boil the carrots long enough and so I ate around them. I wasn't even that hungry; the stress was far too overwhelming. I looked out from my window and saw Indian children talking to each other outside. These were the bulk of my neighbors. I've lived here a couple of years and have never learned any of their names. Eventually, they ran off, doing whatever it is immigrant children do with each other in this country. I looked at my phone. I had more calls I needed to make.

I decided to call my uncle on the way to Katie's. I hit the pavement of the exurb, walking out of my apartment complex and heading towards the little downtown area where she worked that looked like a cozy little town surrounded by a sea of industrial parks. I was never close with my uncle, but a few years ago, I worked for him and we'd always talk politics. His instincts were good, even if everything he believed was wrong.

"Uncle," I said once he picked up.

"Jim," he called me. "How's it going? What's that noise in the background?" He was referring to the zooming traffic outside as I walked the sidewalk near the road.

"It's traffic. I'm walking into town to see Katie since I don't have any work today. I'll move a little bit away from the road so that you can hear me better." I moved down into the grass that sloped down away from the road, walking beside the remnant trees that were once part of whatever massive field or wooded area this exurban area once was just a few decades ago.

"What happened to your car?" he asked with concern.

"Couldn't afford it anymore. Had to choose between that or rent."

"Call me again tomorrow; I can scrounge up something for you if you need some part-time work."

"Sure thing, but I know that's not why you called me."

He chuckled a bit and began to draw out what he had to say, like a child that had a surprise he wanted to show his parents. "What did you think about what Trump said?" It was always politics with my uncle. He knew I had supported Trump in the past, and so whenever we talked in the last three years, it was about that and always that. About how the election was stolen from Trump. About the court cases that were brought against him, his family, and supporters. About the schemes to support him that came and went; every few conversations, there was always a new one. From schemes to overturn long-done election results to schemes to help Trump out to schemes to help Trump take back the White House, there was always something new to put some cheapened hope in. I stopped him before from throwing good money after bad and he still helps me out; the least I can do is hear him out.

"I didn't really see; what's going on?" *I half-lied,* I thought. I always pretended not to follow what was going on, just to hear it from him, but there were often times he knew about stuff I had never heard. Some of it was from the online group he had found, sometimes it was just because I was that checked out.

"Well, Trump is teasing supporting Ivanka running for president instead of him, but it's obvious he's just trying to bait the media. I'm not really crazy about her, I think her husband Jared caused a lot of problems, but like I said, that's just not happening. He's going to run. He has to run. All of these bozos that have been making his life a living hell since he left office, I'm sure he's licking his chops waiting to go HAM on them. He won't be so nice this time around."

"If they stole the election from him last time, why wouldn't they do it this time? More and more Republicans are even talking about using rules to keep him out of the primaries."

"Yeah, they can try. They'll look stupid when they try. But they can try. No, I will admit that we were a little naive in 2020, but things are different this time. You have patriots now who are infiltrating the party and the deep state to make sure the election is run fairly, and against Kamala Harris, Trump is going to win in an absolute blowout. Pretty sure that New York will be in play because of how bad that state has gotten."

I wasn't sure what to say at first. My uncle was a good man, but my family tells me all he talks about now is this, all he watches is the new "independent" news sources that have popped up in the last two years. There's always plans and theories as to what's going on, but the new administration just keeps rolling on with what they're doing. Life just keeps getting harder.

Sensing my silence, he filled the air. "Trust the Plan, Jim. *Be the Plan.* That's all we can do. That's all we can be. Patriots are in place. We're going to get those bastards this time."

"You're not doing anything with them, are you?" I asked, worried that he was operating in some kind of fed-monitored online group now. I pressed him further. "You aren't in any of those QAnon groups or offshoots, are you?" While they were mostly harmless, enough of the splinter groups had been rolled up on fears of shootings from some of the members. I wasn't sure what to believe about that as I don't trust the government to identify an actual terrorist.

"No need. Just enjoy the show. But I will admit that if things get too hard for me, if I get something terminal, I wonder about who I should just go and take out."

"Yeah, well, let's not talk about that on the phone as I'm pretty sure someone is monitoring us."

"I hear that, I hear that. Well, thanks for calling me back; I was just curious what you thought."

"I guess we'll just need to wait and see."

I hung up the call. I was tired of politics. I was tired of politics five years ago when it became apparent what a dog and pony show it all was. I remember what it was like being constantly sick, being constantly made sick by being plugged into the media cycle. Despite being aware of how it all worked and how the stories were crafted and how Trump played upon that cycle, I could never get enough of it. There was always something to hope for and debate, to argue about and lose friends over. As far as I was concerned, I got out in just time.

My feet were starting to get a bit sore as I approached the small town down the street from my exurb. I had not yet gotten used to the walking yet. I spent most of my time in that apartment. If I absolutely needed to go anywhere, I had Katie to take me there.

I like Katie. She's kind. She's pretty. She doesn't have strong opinions on anything that even men should have strong opinions on. She's just a good person. Maybe other men want more, but this is all I ever wanted. She says she doesn't agree with what I believe or once believed, but she's still here. She worries. I tell her not to worry. I fear I've given her reasons to worry.

The town was active as I got down onto the main street. I pulled out my mask and pulled it up to right under my nose, ready to pull it up over if any busybody started to approach. I put my earbuds in to drown out their nose. This has become typical of life in the last four years. The lockdown never ended. COVID never went away. Anyone too loud about how fake the crisis had become quickly found problems in their employment. Society had already separated and atomized further; no one ever really talked to one another, but a person's employment would always remain the field of battle.

Despite the restrictions and despite the people eager to enforce them, how people obeyed, it was always barely minimum, if at all. People were congregated together, looking into shop windows with their masks pulled down. Everyone eyeballed one another, wondering who could snitch and pulling masks up and separating if they got the wrong vibe off a person. *How do people even live like this,* I wondered. We'd gotten used to it, though.

I walked in and around these small crowds as I headed for the cafe Katie worked in. I probably should have just called her, but it seemed more right to just come and see her. I had a feeling I knew what this was about, and if my relationship was going to end then, it wasn't going to be in some distant way, the same way it seemed like everything was ending these days. Plus, I was already starting to go stir-crazy in that apartment; I would take any opportunity to get out of there.

When I arrived at the cafe, the Blob was sitting there. I should have known. His eyes look even beadier now that I was seeing them this close. If you looked at his photo on his social media accounts, there always seemed to be something off about it. Something unreflective, like a shapeshifting vampire. Whatever photo he used took off 50 pounds, and seeing him much closer, he almost seemed to be bursting out of his clothes. For the first time now, I noticed something that made the whole scene even more unsettling. Through his shaggy hair, he was wearing some rather feminine barrettes. I recalled hearing through the grapevine that the Blob had been talking about gender a lot recently. He grinned a crooked smile at me and I felt the desire to pop him well up through my blood.

He waved at me to come over to his table, knowing that I would have to pass by him anyway to get to the counter. I walked over, intending to just pass on by, but stopped to look at him. It was time for me to do what I had been preparing for since the day I knew I might be found out. I removed my earbuds and took a deep breath.

"Hello, James, or should I say Ethan, or should I say Ethnoskate?"

I stared at him without speaking a word.

"I stopped by your apartment earlier, but you weren't there."

I stared, utterly silent.

He furrowed his brow a bit, "I'm almost done with the piece I've written about you for Justice League," he gestured with his fat hands at his laptop, "though I would love it if you had a comment for me. Tell me your side of the story. I'm a journalist; I'm more than fair."

I could feel the anger well up in me, but I just stared. I stared right through him to the back wall and I could sense his discomfort that I was looking past him. He glanced his eyes around, slightly confused. He smirked.

"Don't you want to know how I found you?"

Nothing. I gave him nothing. I would give him nothing. Absolutely nothing. Absolutely nothing at all.

Someone tried to get around us. He seemed to be confused as to what was going on. He covered his coffee with the top of his hand as he scooted past me. The Blob's eyes tracked the man who was moving past and then returned to me, realizing that my gaze had never wavered. I left no expression but eyes that burned through his own small soul.

Now he seemed agitated. He balled one hand up into a fist and then tried the fake pleasantry once more. "Would you like to hear what Katie said? She had some very interesting things to say. You'll probably want to hear them before you talk to her; it might prepare you for it."

I continued to stare at him. He took a deep sigh and looked back at his laptop, as though he were reading something. He glanced back at me, then back at the laptop. It was clear he wasn't really sure what to do. I continued to stand there, making it as uncomfortable as possible with the blank slate on my face. I might've stood there for ten more minutes if I didn't hear the voice of Katie calling to me from the counter. I slowly turned toward her and walked away, leaving my back to the Blob and never turning back.

I approached Katie, trying to shake the experience of seeing the Blob here off my shoulders. She bent slightly to the side, probably to look at him. I raised my head and looked at her with softer eyes. I saw her purse her lip as she took stock of me. She turned to another woman behind the counter and said, "I'm taking my 15 minute break." The woman nodded and Katie led me out through the cafe to the back behind the cafe.

She turned around and folded her arms once we were outside. "What's going on, Jim? Are you in trouble?"

"Probably. Did you say anything to the Blob?"

"What?" She was bewildered.

"The fat guy, the journalist. What did you say to him?"

"I didn't say anything! I did what you said if someone asks about you and just told him no comment. He kept trying to play your stupid podcast to me and asking if I recognized your voice, but I told him he needed to order something or get out of line. Then he tried to arrange a time we could talk after work. I had Big Tom make him order, but he left. Then he came back and he's been sitting there for about an hour or so. Why? Did he tell you I said something?"

I slumped against the wall of the building and let out a breath of air. "Yes, basically. I think he was just trying to confirm my voice for himself. Someone else who got doxed by him said he does stuff like that; pretends to have more information than he actually does. He might still publish or submit what he has anyway, especially if other people confirmed for him, but we'll just have to keep denying and operating like we don't know what they're talking about."

She rubbed her temples. "Jim, this is a level of paranoia I don't think I'm ready to live with."

"There's nothing to be paranoid about anymore. He publishes what he thinks he's got, we just ignore it. We deny everything. Let them prove I've done anything. That life is far behind me and I'm never going to acknowledge it to them."

She looked like she was on the verge of tears. "You aren't still doing that dumb podcast, are you? Don't lie to me."

I looked at her, a bit confused. "Katie, I haven't had a microphone since before I met you. They're just chasing the high of being able to dox Internet edgelords and combing through the archive of anything they think is notable enough. I'm a nobody. Just a white guy who wants to live a normal life with the woman I love."

She pursed her lip again as a tear ran down her cheek. She rubbed her face with her hands and snorted. She walked over to me and just put her arms around. She rested her head against my chest and sniffled. She squeezed. I put my arms around her and just held her. She felt very warm. It felt very nice. I liked this more than everything I thought had mattered five years ago.

She looked up at me, her face beet red and embarrassed.

"What's wrong?" I asked her.

It took her a moment to bring herself to answer. My heart stopped until she said it. "I spit in his coffee." I burst out laughing. "I shouldn't have done that; it was wrong, but I couldn't stand to hear the things he said about you." I squeezed her tighter.

"James."

"Yes?"

"Is there a future for us? It's not going to be like this forever, will it? I don't just mean the paranoia about our lives being ruined because you did something stupid on the Internet because of Trump or whatever; I just mean all of this. I'm so tired. I'm so tired of it all. The last four years have been election, lockdown, and we're back to election again. Nothing seems to change unless it's just getting worse. We can't keep living like this."

"I promise you, Katie, it won't always be like this." I couldn't be certain that would ever be the truth, but it felt right.

We stayed in our embrace until she finally said, "Ee need to go back inside, my break is going to end. I'll see you tonight?"

"Yeah, I'll see you tonight."

We walked back in through the backdoor and she took her spot back behind the corner. The Blob was still at the table and he nodded at me with that same sweaty face and that same crooked smile. A flicker on a television screen in the corner near the front door caught my eye. The chyron on the television read that Trump was now teasing that he'd jump into the race but make Ivanka his running mate. I sighed. More conversations with friends and family to come. More grift, more kabuki theater, more tricks and schemes. More nothing.

I started to walk past the Blob, then stopped. I looked at him again, less staring this time. I took in his shape and almost briefly felt sorry for him and the life he lived. Almost. He looked at me expectantly, like I might finally say something. I looked around at the mostly empty cafe. Those who were in had socially distanced themselves far to the other ends. I wondered if they sat as far away from him as they could on purpose. I looked back at Katie, who was back on shift and fulfilling an order. I looked at the Blob's table and to his coffee. He had taken the lid off. He continued with that wicked smile. I opened my mouth, then spit into his coffee. Without waiting for his reaction, I walked out.

I could hear him struggle to get up and I could hear him shouting angrily at me, but I walked quickly out that door without looking back again. I walked swiftly down the sidewalk and dipped down different side streets to lose him. I eventually got back on the main road and the long walk home. I walked with my shoulders broad and proud. It felt like there were no more victories in this world, but I would take that one.

I stared off into that uncertain orange sun. This was the rest of my life. Past that sun, there was only darkness ahead. I welcomed it, though, simply for the promise that would lie once the night was done. I thought of Katie, her warm embrace. I thought of children and their possibilities. I thought of Trump. At the end of it all, he would disappear, like he'd never been there at all. All that remained it seemed was myself.

That'll have to do.

FOUR MORE TEARS

by Taurine Dealer

There is an online theory which you may have encountered. It states that Donald Trump's 2016 victory was a fluke, a glitch in the system that was never meant to happen. This supposed error produced certain results which some would say were still in-line with the agenda of the powers that be.

One such event took place in early December of 2017, when the Trump Administration decided to officially recognize Jerusalem as the Capital of I.S.R.A.E.L. A move that was—in my humble opinion—relatively Cricket-Chirped by the media at large, at least when compared to how celebrated it would have been if it had taken place under any other administration.

One may only venture to guess why this was so, though this guessing wouldn't have to go on for too long, seeing as this looked like just another example of how the network talking heads refused to paint Trump in any sort of positive light, in this case, for their Jewish and evangelical audiences. So curious was this—at best—lukewarm reception, that in fact, one CNN politics article called the move a "break with tradition" where—again—had it occurred under a hypothetical Clinton administration, I suspect many an Israeli would have been sent into dancing fits by all the headlines and reassurances from so-called ForPol experts. But I digress.

The fluke theory posits further that the system needs to self-correct, hence fitting in the apparent electoral fraud that took place on November 3rd of 2020, the true result and consequences of which are—amazingly—yet to be fully seen by the time this is being written. Summoning all its might, it seems that the powers that be aligned themselves with the mission of stomping out a second contiguous Trump term, and many would say that they, without a doubt, would take steps to prevent any other further reelection down the line, whatever that may take.

The validity of this last part of the theory is of course up for debate, but I would dare to say with complete confidence that the vast majority of people simply agree with it, almost without question, regardless of where they stand on Trump's presidency. If anything was made sufficiently clear, it was that the media, both American and international, seemed perplexingly and overwhelmingly inclined to attack him with every satire, parody, joke and bit of bad press that they could muster; they concocted a tale of collusion with the Russian government, which included golden showers from Kremlin courtesans and BDSM-like obeisance to Vladimir Putin. They absolutely hate the man's fat orange guts with a burning passion, one that resulted in what can only be described from here to history as a series of spite-driven, schizophrenic episodes of whitewashing for the likes of John McCain and George W. Bush, as they were then reimagined as agreeable paragons of Republican decency to be contrasted to Trump's unfiltered and informal demeanor, much in spite of his—quite frankly—tepid policies.

It wasn't just the media and celebrities who were content to direct the barrage of vitriol against our most serene and august cheesy puff. Certain figures in politics were, and continue to be, more than happy to mock and antagonize him. Chief among them, perhaps, is Justin Trudeau, the first boy band prime minister of Canada.

To make this idea that the entire system is set against him seem even more perplexing, one need only look again at Trump's comparatively tame policy record and realize that his administration hasn't really gotten away with much besides his turbulent Tweeting fits and brash comments to the press. In a 2017 policy briefing for the Centre for International Governance Innovation (CIGI), one Susan Schadler writes, with a single eyebrow raised, how smoothly the relationship between the Orange-White House and the IMF had gone up until that point. Part of the reasons, she says, relates to the "technical" nature of the IMF's work, leading to a relatively sparse headline presence (save some high-profile cases) which simply does not tend to overlap with Trump's propensity to Tweet about hot button topics that would primarily result in engagement with his base. However, this is not to say that all has been quiet ever since, because the following year, the IMF issued a "warning" that an escalation of Trump's tariffs over trade would hurt global growth by a whopping 0.5 percent.

Later that year, Bloomberg would publish the following headline (which is best read out loud with a single raised fist in a solemn expression): "Trump Snubs Global Order Again as U.S. Rejects IMF Funding Boost." Hilarious.

The sort of headline that results in Trump's sympathizers being reassured in their continued support and in his detractors sinking deeper into their rabid hatred of his so-called isolationist policies. His entire presidency is peppered by these double-edged headlines; one must wonder if this was intentional, or simply the result of an impotent journalistic class unable to muster any real, damnable controversies against a man almost equally impotent in realizing the vision he promised to his voters and true believers.

The IMF is far from the only international organism that exchanged words of controversy with Trump. Back again in 2017, German Chancellor Angela Merkel gave an alarming—yet limp—election rally speech in Munich (from a beer hall, no less) in which she stated somewhat ominously that "the era in which we could fully rely on others is over to some extent." She then added, "We Europeans truly have to take our fate into our own hands; naturally in friendship with the United States of America, in friendship with Great Britain, as good neighbors with whoever, also with Russia and other countries." It's not too complicated to read between the lines of those statements, as Frau Merkel was fresh off of a G7 summit where Trump declined to recommit to the Paris climate accord, rubbing salt upon the wound inflicted by the first few Brexit negotiations in March of that year. A *Politico* article published in the wake of that particular summit had a strange quote that perfectly encapsulated this sort of hyperbolic reaction to Trump. It read as follows:

> *"'There were fears: would he attend the G7?' one senior EU official said, noting that Trump's election had called into question 'the entire Western architecture, post Second World War.'"*

Very strange! The supposed senior E.U. official remains unidentified and it is unclear what they meant by "Trump's election." However, it does exemplify the strong dramatic flair and fearmongering that spun furiously around his administration, almost as if to hammer into the public the idea that voting for a political "outsider" or a populist was bad and that going against the grain of internationalism only brings us closer to scary apocalyptic scenarios.

In spite of the alarmist rhetoric peddled by the liberal and leftist mouthpieces of the globalist lever-pullers, the fact of the matter is that few (if any at all) of his administration's foreign policy plays caused any real lasting damage to the vaunted "world order" of *Bloomberg* or to the "Western architecture" of the unknowable senior E.U. official. Why, then, is a second Trump term so anathema? What is ever so threatening to the keepers of the status quo? I believe it is not Trump himself that worries them, but the ethos of defiance that became apparent in the wake of his campaign and subsequent electoral victory. Many people did not vote for Trump because they believed him or even supported his ambitions and projects; they voted for Trump because they loathed the alternative, because they wanted their discontent to spill into the streets and Internet forums. They wanted to laugh in the face of the pamphletarianism of the United Nations and the European Union. I believe it wasn't just hundreds or thousands, but perhaps millions in America who, in 2016 and 2020 went—together with some true believers—to the voting booths for the sake of spite, a small vengeance against the managerial class and the porn-addled commissaries that enforce the sodomite state of consciousness. It is this very same managerial class, along with their media personalities and preacher-journalists, who feel the most threatened by the idea that the common man hates them and wants nothing to do with their vision of the world. The days of the conspiring political acrobats and the polymaths with links to aristocracy are quickly fading away; those people are being replaced by new-money plebeians who are at best described as overeducated and lacking in any real intelligence, who derive their authority from credentialism. These people do well in being afraid; they should be living in fear of their power waning.

It is worth asking the following question: will they allow this insubordination to go on unpunished? If you believe like I, and many others, that the 2020 American elections were rigged against Trump, then part of that answer has already been given. They will go to any lengths, including a very obvious and transparent system-wide cheat, to stop him. Who is to say his life isn't in real danger from here on out? God only knows what the Pentagon trusted him with, and Trump's loose cannon attitude might just make him especially dangerous now that he knows some juicy state secrets. It is perfectly understandable why many expect Trump to get JFKed sooner rather than later, and I think it's possible he himself expects this. At one point or another (particularly in 2016-2017), it seemed that a lot of people in certain online circles (namely, Frog Twitter and its adjacencies) were expecting assassination attempts against Trump, or at least against members of his family.

This obviously never happened, much to the surprise of some. Instead of a dramatic and sudden death to fuel another half a century of conspiratorial enthusiasm and general distrust of the intelligence agencies, the mass media machine worked overtime to utilize Trump's controversial image as proof that the boogeyman of white supremacy and far-right extremism was not only alive and well, but also needed to be eradicated and prevented by any means necessary, opening minds up towards more regulations on free speech, more intervention by supranational entities, and the role of big tech corporations in preserving "democracy" and "decency" in the public discourse. I do not wish to imply that Trump belongs in any way to a form of controlled opposition, because I don't think so. Neither do I wish to downplay what his 2016 victory meant for right-wing political movements, as well as the overall trend of dissidence and resentment towards globalist orthodoxy that seems to be gaining strength. Nevertheless, it remains an important point to acknowledge that the collective hissy fits of the narrative-makers haven't been completely wasted. Many creepy precedents have been set: never before was it so clear (to the common man at least) that companies such as Facebook and Twitter had very clear political agendas. Their willingness to censor private individuals for wrongthink extended further to the point of temporarily censoring officials and even government-wide organizations within the Trump administration, and as recently as December of 2020, the company confirmed their willingness—if not their intention—to outright ban Trump from their platform after Inauguration Day 2021 should he prove troublesome and unpalatable to their chain-yankers. This is all assuming that Joe Biden does assume the presidency, that is.

Wink.

So while all of this huffing and puffing has been going on, what has the much-vaunted deep state done? Seemingly, they hedged their bets. Between bouts of fruitless inquiries, investigations, and threats of impeachment, they helped themselves to Trump's provocative attitude and quite easily turned him into a real-life supervillain they could target with the propaganda machine at their disposal; what better way is there to encroach upon the rights and liberties of the common man than to trick them into willingly giving them up in order to combat the perceived menace of radical madmen? A play that anyone living in a country that has "fought" terrorism is more than familiar with, and it is of little wonder that terms such as "fake news" and "hate speech" have become so paramount to modern public discourse, and how many companies and governments have vowed to combat these evils at any cost.

It bears mentioning that Trump was far from the only signal of mass discontent towards the globalist project, if not in action, then at the very least in vocal intent. Marine Le Pen, Matteo Salvini, and even Vladimir Putin are some other key active figures that come to mind most when discussing these topics, regardless of how true and how effective they may or may not be, of course. Still, there are many others who share Trump's cheeky populist slant that draws so much ire from the liberal thought police, the most notorious among them being perhaps the infamous Jair Bolsonaro, who had a penchant for re-Tweeting fan art of himself next to anime/manga icon Son Goku, and as recently as November of 2020, he addressed his fellow Brazilians on live television, telling them to stop acting like a "country of faggots" in regards to the coronavirus pandemic that has taken a heavy toll on the South American nation...this was an order of magnitude beyond outrageous when compared to anything that Donald Trump has ever said. Then again, Bolsonaro is not commander-in-chief of the world's strongest military.

The defenders of public decency, who at one time were social conservatives railing against Pokémon and death metal, now rail against masturbation abstinence and fundamental biological principles. As upside down as the world seems, it would perhaps look less insane if it weren't for controversial political figures that cause so much psychic stress on the faggot pundits of enlightened liberalism. This is a good thing. It is good that they show their hand so openly. It is good when they sperg out like the insecure teenaged neurotics and petty narcissists that they are. It is good when they fly into effeminate hysterics—at times even crying live on air—over some fat orange douchebag that doesn't take them seriously, because they absolutely should not be taken seriously by anyone, regardless of how real a threat their intentions pose. They do not yet realize this; they cannot possibly imagine how their fearmongering and crying is actually making them look stupid and weak. This is a wonderful gift; take advantage of it.

I do not know if we'll ever see four more years of Trump; whether from 2021 or 2024, I have doubts about it, but there can be no doubt in my mind that the past four years have been a—useful—spectacle to behold. Perhaps this sounds callous and detached because I myself am not an American, and maybe I would be much more bitter towards it all if that were the case, so if you're American, let me assure you that I sympathize with you, but please take into consideration that that the U.S. is the dominant cultural hegemony of the world. The list of countries that live under America's shadow is too long to discuss, and anything that happens there ripples and is mirrored elsewhere in unexpected ways. This is why I believe that understanding what has happened thus far is so important, because it has clearly laid out for everyone the mechanisms by which power will be consolidated further at the cost of the common man's (especially if they happen to be white) quality of life, dignity, and freedom. Just today, I had to come back to this piece of writing at the last minute to mention how four IMF researchers casually dropped a paper about the possible advantages in allowing financial institutions access to your Internet browsing history and online purchases for purposes that no doubt range from the *cough* "noble" to the sinister. Keep in mind, however, that I do not wish to imply that "because Trump got elected, now the enemy has revealed itself," but there is no doubt that the zeitgeist of political incorrectness and general hostility between worldviews that he so perfectly crystalized has either forced or at least facilitated a push towards these ideas being brought to the discourse, if only to test the waters and maybe acclimatize the public to what has been part of the plan all along. And that is my closing thought, because I don't really think it matters what happens to Trump from here on out; what really matters is what I have learned because of these "interesting times" with him at the helm of the world's premier cultural superpower. I saw that they want you angry and clouded. I saw that they want you constantly outraged and anxious. They want you addicted to the endless cycle of terror and entertainment pressed by their propaganda machine. In essence, they want you to be bent over and suffering and afraid.

So here's to more bitching, here's to four more tears.

TRUMP, UNDEAD TECHNO-MASSA

by Pain Singh

2045: Jared awakens in pools of his own sweat and spittle. In the past two decades, the white American population has dive bombed to 40 percent and in its wake left a stirring of white identity. Court magi in the reign of the Bibi-Kamala administration realized that attempts to crush such identity would be found futile and opted to trot out the silver-tongued slave merchants and brewed concoctions, wherein the water was spiked with a poison composed of Gadsden flags and pocket Constitutions. Even in this elixir, the cracks had begun to show.

In a haze, Jared reaches for his phone; it's been ringing for the past hour. He clutches the speaker close to his ear, but all he can make out on the other end of the line is the sound of pennies hitting the floor. The sounds are rhythmic, as if they were a Semitic version of Chinese water torture. The regularity of the metallic clangs were hypnotizing, and he felt himself slowly losing grip over himself. The screen shatters against the bedroom linoleum; shaking and clutching his own chest, he fears the dark deeds of what's to come.

2025: the senior Trump, after having lost his second presidential bid to the Kamala-Romney Administration, had since been under house arrest in his golden tower. Nearing the eve of summer, he was found dead, having collapsed amidst shards of glass and spilt-over bottles of amphetamines. After his second presidential loss, the Cultic Legions of QAnon, now driven into a mad rage, fedpoasted like none other had ever dared before and rushed to the aid of their emperor. They experienced initial victories, culminating in the seizure of the White House and replacing Fort Knox with reels filled with thousands of hours of Groyper-Ali Akbar cuck porn. The Legions under General Jones were ultimately smashed under a sea of H-1B turmeric spell-casters, Castizo Futurist Centurions, and animal-human hybrid African Chimera. Some blamed the defeat on the wignats who refused the QAnon baptism (complaining it entailed shoving and swallowing slips of paper in one's mouth like a golem), while America First brushed the accusation aside, assuring the trad e-Cath-cum-groypers it was all just a metaphor representing every patriot as a ballot box (thanks for all the Super Chats, kings). Others who claim themselves as being an intellectual aristocratic elite blamed the interference of a breakaway Super Racialist Parapsychological Prussian elite who have held the American reins of power since the 1890's.

A funeral was held in New York, replete with all the due honours granted to an ex-president in hopes that such displays would quell a rebirth of further uprisings by Q Cultists, who had by then been fought back to guerilla bands spouting rhetoric about harassing power stations. Many of varying Internet fame had gone all in on avenging the to-be American emperor. Among them was Curt Doolittle of former propertarianism fame, who had by then reappeared onto the scene after a cozy contractor career of planning color revolutions for USG, though control over his bladder had worsened; amidst open calls for violent action and brutal civil war, this caused more than one embarrassing moment during public meetings. During his funeral, Trump's body was never shown to the public before being cremated. His ashes were then sprinkled into the sea off the end of a carrier. Some commentators joked about it being the Boston Tea Party of the New America.

In the mainstream of American politics, none were more convinced of malpractice by the elites than the remnants of the exhausted Church of QAnon. The Qope, the head priest of Q (whom the majority of Q devotees still recognized), cried to his followers from the Facebook boomer pages and to what was once Protestant America for a great jihad on the Chi-Com occupied government (CHOG). Few beyond high ranking Israeli intelligence operatives, the rabbinical councils, and the remnants of the Internet Nazis not lined up and shot by the Q Legions suspected the nature of the hidden events taking place in the passing of the senior Trump's natural death.

Minutes after his passing, elite teams of Mossad had broken into Trump Towers to secure the body. After having slipped it away in an unmarked limousine, the body was sped away to an airstrip, where it was loaded on to a stolen SR-71 Blackbird from the 70's. It was flown straight to Tel Aviv, where it was then commandeered by teams of doctors, scientists, and rabbinic scholars who attempted the near impossible task of reviving and saving what they could of the corpse.

2045: holding back tears, Jared downs another bottle of vodka to try and steel his nerves for what was to come. After landing in Tel Aviv, he's joined by a team of bodyguards with whom he speeds away to a patch of northern Israel now known as the Trump Heights. As they approach the remains of an ancient ruin, he starts to feel the need to send videos of himself jerking off to minors; confused, the driver passes him some pills to suppress his libido and explains that they are coming upon some transported ruins of Sodom and Gomorrah.

From outside the facility, he could already hear rabbis chanting, the piercing screams of chickens, and cries of Palestinian children all rising to a brain-melting crescendo as he neared the main chamber. Choking on smoke and the smells of decomposing flesh, Jared clung onto the walls when he noticed they were all decorated in the art style of Cleon Peterson. *A nice touch,* he thought to himself, taking particular time to appreciate an image of white figures being spat and stomped on.

As he descended further into the Tartarus maze, nothing, not even parties with Epstein or the Freemasonic blood rituals, could have prepared him for the horror of the main hall. Suspended in a mucous-like dark fluid and held in a semi-frozen state hung what remained of his father-in-law. He gawked at the alien machines that drilled into his spinal column and the wires that sent electric shocks and nutrients straight to the brain and nervous system; clearly he was more metal than man. The dense web of machinery and circuitry was etched over completely with Kabbalistic runes. He would become all-too-familiar with this promethean demon of technology that the teams of scientists and rabbis called "cybermancy."

Jared had been sent to awaken this new iron golem. He found himself surrounded by familiar faces, from Dr. Rumer and Bibi Netanyahu to Ben Shapiro beaming with shame and tears in his eyes. *Rightfully so,* he thought. Him, Prager, Rubin, and the rest of the campus conservative

Intellectual Dark Web had failed to do their jobs, making all of this action necessary.

They were gathered here for the same reason. After the defeat of QAnon, the cult withered away as the state imprisoned and "deradicalized" its followers, promising they could return to regular society if they turned themselves in. The most dedicated, refusing to go quietly, carried out attacks on Democrat and non-Trumpian Republicans; in the words of the Qope, they ended up as martyrs for the emperor. The rest either managed to slip into regular society or retreated away, forming hidden but powerless communities. Jaded by these events and having had the cultic hysteria worn off, its members had begun to realize they had the wool pulled over their eyes.

In subsequent decades, the pressure bared down on white Americans only exploded, culminating in attacks on their neighborhoods not dissimilar from scenes familiar to South Africa. In the minds of those bearing the attacks, the idea that politics offered viable solutions was little more than a joke. Not long after did the GOP and its Trumpian holdouts begin to preach that reparations were a conservative position and that the attacks could have been prevented if the once-minorities had been treated better.

The tribesmen gathered here had truly run out of ideas. To stem the rising tide of white nationalism and buy them more time to shift American demographics even further, those gathered around the dead mechanized remains of Donald Trump planned on reviving him, and with him, Q. White identity would be allowed to be mainstreamed, but only by it entailing a loyalty to Q and the now truly God-Emperor back from the dead.

As the ritual commenced, the rabbis began to chant their demonic hymns, scientists rushed to turn on the energy, making the runes glow, and soon he started to awaken, the new white techno-massa back from the undead. Ever quickly as the foundations of the ruins shook and as the robotics came alive, there appeared from the depths a voice. First, a whisper sounding like the fraying of wires and circuits and building to a raspy metal clang. Tears leapt from the eyes of those gathered as it spoke:

"TRUST…THE…PLAN."

CRYPTIDS OF THE SPECTACLE; OR, TRUMPIAN AESTHETICS VS. NEOLIBERAL KITSCH

by Gio Penn

It is often said that we are in an age of information war; an asymmetrical form of digital knowledge-production warfare fought exclusively on enemy territory. But what is the info-war about? It is true what Michel Foucault posited a base insight, but one that drips with profundity: that insight being that knowledge itself is a creation of power, how discursive power creates new forms of knowledge, new specializations, new dictates on how to even receive knowledge, and whom should, and in what amount, etc. We can say that power/knowledge is a vital insight because the operational discourses of society dictate certain courses of action, and beyond that how knowledge is produced itself, and how one is meant to interpret certain forms of knowledge depending on its sources.

The "open" liberal global society relies on "expertism" that is only bestowed upon the few. The premise of a liberal post-Enlightenment society is that knowledge itself is created objectively, and for utilitarian purposes, but we can see that any "fact-checker" is easily shown to be partisan, and any Tweet-warning of disinformation—or in other words, information that is "disputed"—highlights this even more.

Let us truly get to the heart of the matter: in my opinion, the info-war is really a foil for a spiritual war, a war of one's inner most convictions, principles, thumos and pathos. Our political dispositions often dictate our existential and epistemological dispositions, and our spiritual dispositions are not far upstream from politics. As we know, politics has invaded the everyday, the "they," the personal is not just the political, but everything is the political in the age of Trump's "Weimar" dissolution of the social order. And this is where things get interesting, because in the framework of power/knowledge, resistances to power and counter-sources of power crop up eventually. But if the subject has been in toto consumed by politics, and furthermore the subject itself is created by, and shot through with power, the soul of mankind withers on the rotting vines of chasing the next political spectacle. The collective soul often finds meagre and bulimic subsistence in the political spectacle itself.

So, you ask, what does this have to do with the state of art after the Trump era? The works of art of an era often reveal the lesions of the soul like nothing else, and as everything has become spectacle in the age of Trumpian hyperreality, everything in a way has become wonderous, hideous, terrifyingly scintillating art.

War produces art like no other, and when life becomes a virtual political battlefront without end, where one's identity itself is a political (and warlike) statement, art never ceases to come into being. Foucault reversed Clausewitz's famed assertion by stating that instead of war being politics by another means, politics is in fact war by another means:

> *"...we can invert Clausewitz's proposition and say that politics is the continuation of war by other means...the role of political power is perpetually to use a sort of silent war to reinscribe that relationship of force, and to reinscribe its institutions, economic inequalities, language, and even the bodies of individuals. This is the initial meaning of our inversion of Clausewitz's aphorism—politics is the continuation of war by other means."*[1]

What is overlooked is the relationship between this war of power inscribing itself onto the very functions of modern life and subjectivity, and the role of the work of art itself. What the Trump, and soon to be post-Trump, era has revealed is this naked force of artistic production in service of power. Not simply a hierarchical node of power in the office of the POTUS, but rather the decentralized, diffused apparatuses of power which creates the very forces of social relations themselves.

Yet they are held together by discursive strands, and the ability of

---

[1] Foucault, Michael. *"Society Must Be Defended"*: Lectures at the *Collège de France,* ed. Mauro Bertani and Alessandro Fontana, trans. David Macey (New York: Picador, 2003), 47.

liverse institutions and the apparatus of power to operate in unison has
›een laid bare in the wake of Trumpian politics, like a body working with
ıll its immune functions and systems across the whole to expel a viral
ıntigen (forgive me for the analogy given the circumstances of 2020)
›rovoking a response. Trump, if anything, despite his flaws and foibles and
ailings, has been a near perfect antigen that has provoked an endless and
lizzyingly hysterical response. The contemporary art world may not be
›n the radars of most people glued to other institutions of power, like the
nainstream media, and the Hollywood celebrity (cult)ure industry, but it is
›eerless in its rapid and hysterical institutional response to Trumpism.

The CAW vs. The Trumpenreich

It is of a vital importance to acknowledge that the art made in our
ime is within the confines and service of the same war of power, of power/
nowledge itself. And if anything, the spectacle of Trump (we shall cover
his soon) has been marked by a boom period of activist art that not
he Bush or even Nixon years had met with previously. But what is the
›utsider, the folk, the counter-aesthetics to this miasma of turgid, kitschy,
epetitive, zombie-formalist activist art? The CAW (contemporary art
vorld) has produced gallery exhibits filled with works given new life and
"relevance" surrounding the aura of Trump. But these works are almost
ılways typical, and in a way not even that confrontational, but rolling over
nto a monotonous voice of official, and sanctioned side-taking.

One needs to only stroll through the digital galleries and numerous
›ublications, articles, and lectures by artists and art critics, matrons of the
CAW to see the apoplectic and unison voice of protest art these last four
vears. Exhibits such as the "emergency" art collective show "Abortion is
Normal (2019-2020)" (which I have reviewed extensively[2]) held in protest
›f the waves of pro-life legislation made easier to pass through under
he Trump administration. Here, we see the typical crass and tepid feats
›f feminist and multicultural protest art, which mixes grating appeals
o sympathy for the plight of infanticide enthusiasts and a supreme
riumphalism at the current radical liberal values sanctioned by every
ultural institution. There are numerous works that worship secular saints
such as Ruth Bader Ginsburg, flying in the face of the plastic and painted

[2] https://gioscontentcorner.wordpress.com/2020/10/19/bodily-profanations-part-1-3/

enemy of all things Trump.

There are appropriations of religious symbology, inverted and grotesquely pantomimed in the service of the postmodern resurrection of the "Terrible Mother" archetype. No doubt to relive that retro-futurist epoch of the 80's that Trump represents, fighting the walking-dead enemy of the religious right like the feminist matriarchs of yore. With glitzy and decadent protest art hallmarks such as slogans made as gallery pieces, paintings done in fluids, paintings of genitals (such as the infamous Trump portrait with a vagina instead of a mouth), billboards and sculptures of hot red lips affirming an empowering shout of defiance.

There are gatherings of anti-Trump protest art, such as the book Not Normal: Art in the Age of Trump (2020)[3]which gives the best overview of protest art in the Trump era: pieces of paintings, mixed media and sculpture, violent, grotesque, often libidinally-charged caricatures of protest art that are numerous, yet so easy to comprehend and guess as to the intent and meaning of.

Turgid liberal politi-kitsch pieces meant to demonize whatever the artist and art critic sees as the fallen period of the American democratic project the Orange Führer represents. These works in themselves reveal Trump's "post-truth" visage as an imago, an icon of vacuous space that can be filled with whatever meaning one likes; pieces that display Trump as a dictator, literally filled with words such as "liar" and "con artist." Images and paintings of protesters, the worship of sacred identity groups such as migrants that are being oppressed by the ever-present wispy orange-haired gaze of a plastic demon. Trump holding a Bible stating it is "his weapon," Trump as Goya's Saturn eating Lady Liberty. Trump having sex with Vice President Pence, Putin, and Mitch McConnell, a MAGA Klansman hood, among other vile and provocative displays. As one book reviewer states it:

> *"The art in the age of Trump collectively mirrors the sharp edges of our current plight that reflects the destructive passions of our feverishly un-American baby emperor, amplifying the critical issues that we face, which leave our fellow comrades in continual depravity without hope."*[4]

One only hopes that quaint but cringe-worthy inclusion of "comrades"

[3] Gutfreund, Karen. M. http://karengutfreund.com/not-normal-art-in-the-age-of-trump/

[4] Ibid.

is stated with a bit of irony. Another less-than-critical reviewer states:

> *"They (the artists) unapologetically amplify clearly observed objections to this administration's policies and Trump's propaganda that pushes a fictional reality that serves only him..."*

In a word, bourgeois liberal blackpilling in contemporary art form.

Behind the intellectual work of these critics are the reality that these works only come off as LARPing fervent and passionate outrage. Pointing out incessant and one-dimensional statements, however seemingly clever that they might be, is nothing more than that which we have heard for the last four years, and will continue to hear: that Trump is a unique threat to whatever vague and nebulous "American," "democratic," liberal values the blue empire[5] chooses to instrumentalize now. Trump and his supporters are fascists (historians are even in on this grift[6]) and as the protest works highlight—despite their intersectional and perspectival nature—are merely curated to drown the viewer with a singular point of view, that this time in history is unique, and every artist is at pains to hysterically emphasize this. That there has been a seismic disruption in the order of things, and like antibodies attacking a viral invader, the CAW, like other blue empire institutions, must act accordingly and attack with all its might.

The art world of almost every epoch has been at least in some ways at service of the power structures and constrictors placed upon it by certain assumptions about the nature of reality. Only at crucial moments of decay and collapse has creativity in art arisen and new epistemes have been formed. The reality of art being instrumentalized by power/knowledge is a feature, not a offshoot. The romantic visions of the iconoclastic, almost childishly defiant and rebellious artist is a relatively recent invention conceptually, if anything almost crafted into a ready-made marketing tool. As Parallax Optics states:

> *"Progressivism holds a libidinal attraction for contemporary artists because they are drawn to power and social status, in particular when it is connected to virtuous pursuits,*

---

[5] Hall, Jordan. 2018. https://medium.com/deep-code/understanding-the-blue-church-e4781b2bd9b5

[6] https://www.cnn.com/2019/10/02/opinions/trump-impeachment-unprecedented-cobbs-longley-osgood-suri/index.html

such as championing equality, diversity and environmental issues. As a neo-religious constellation of moral coordination points, progressivism forms a complete, self-contained belief system. At a structural level, its axiomatic constructs shape the epistemological landscape progressives inhabit, informing their assumptions on both a conscious and subconscious level."[7]

The dream of ethical consumption and ethical production of the work of art hangs in the background of neoliberal kitsch in all its forms, with its lionization of certain identities and its demonization of others reigning supreme. The glowing assumptions made about instrumentalized activist art in the Trump and post-Trump age by critics (as we have seen above) fits perfectly with this assessment of a self-contained world, like the heliospheric world encapsulated by the church in medieval times, to which art at the time followed and informed this world. For in art, the possible becomes actual, and the actual crosses over into mythos.

But what of art in the post-Trump age specifically? Predictions made by critics such as Robert Hughes states "when critics try to fish out the crystal ball, they are almost invariably wrong. I don't think there's ever been such a rush towards the insignificant in the name of the historical future as there has been within the last 15 years."[8] Bear in mind that this statement was made in the 80's but is just as relevant today. The shibboleths of woke activist art is here to stay, but Trump and Trumpism as a unique subject matter has produced a furious and creative response by the CAW, however retreaded this response is. Trump the Imago may fade as subject matter in the coming years, if not brought out once in a while to remind people whenever a serious politically rightward candidate arises. The failure of the woke artist's imagination is that this is somehow an exceptional time and that their art reflects an implicit conceit that if there is enough attention and denunciations paid to the "crimes" of Trump and his supporters, both real and imagined, that things will go back to "normal" and the order of things will be restored.

The CAW, like other blue empire organs, thinks that there is a

---

7 Parallax Optics. 2017. https://parallaxoptics.com/2017/08/24/progressivism-neo-religion-of-the-contemporary-art-world/

8 Hughes, Robert. "Shock of the New, Episode 8." 1980. https://www.youtube.com/watch?v=XXGbyjUMjNE

"normal" to return to, the basic globo-neoliberal consensus on what constitutes the "progress" our planet and the populations inhabiting it are moving towards. But what we are seeing is a total aesthetic, cultural and artistic Balkanization that will only intensify after the wake of Trump the image, along with the political Balkanization everyone pays attention too. Little attention is paid to this aesthetic split or fragmentation, and an even more sizable and clear-cut fragmentation than the standard collapse of metanarratives in postmodernity.

However, the center of the ruling neoliberal aesthetic regime is intact, as it is not a total fragmentation, but a crazing and splitting around the marginal periphery; at the center lies the forces of globalized neoliberal deculturation, which kitschifies and uproots every aspect of culture, and turns aesthetic and the culture industry production against culture itself. For instance, multiculturalism in art and culture is at the core of deculturation, for it precisely upends the fabric of genuine localist and minoritarian cultures in favor of an empty, de-signifying mono universalist perspective. A hidden totalitarian perspective that just so happens to embody all the core assumptions of post-enlightenment liberal modernity worldwide.[9]

The CAW is just as much a force of deculturalization as the global Hollywood and pop culture industries, and art made during and now after the Trump age is evidence of this: we see endless streams of cheap and vivid activist art-fodder pictures of woke protestors, and the transportation of agitprop dialectical images across the globe. It was the aesthetic and pop activist art of American politics, not just the concepts and the political categorizations, which carried with it the globalization and colonization of American domestic politics around the globe. Protests against Trumpism, whether they be in the flavors of BLM or the Women's March, happened simultaneously around the world, from London and Tokyo to Buenos Aires, Sydney to Johannesburg.[10] It was the media-romanticized images and art of America's domestic situations as interpreted by bourgeois leftist artists that made this colonization and deculturation of local politics around the world happen, and this trend will continue.

---

[9] Botz-Borstein, Thorsten. *The New Aesthetics of Deculturation, Neoliberalism, Fundamentalism and Kitsch.* (London, New York, Oxford: Bloomsbury Academic, 2019): pg. 144-145.

[10] https://www.bbc.com/news/av/world-52967551

But the other side is the fragmentary margins, the aesthetic periphery that represents a small, but not insignificant rebellion and pushback against the center. However, they too, like the woke artists no longer possessing the plastic demon of Trump, will lose steam without a powerful image-as-personification. But the trends in their direction, as well as the center's, will only intensify and not abate in the near and distant future post-Trump.

Politics and Info-Warfare as Aesthetic Performativity

Neoliberal kitsch and the forces of deculturation, as we have seen, are an integral part of politics and political/activist performativity. George Floyd touring the world holographically is itself an example of deculturation, as well as the endless paintings, street art, sculptures, and installation pieces. A hallmark concept of neoliberal or radical liberal kitsch is that it must appropriate the themes of mythos and religion to invert and overcome them. Digital, media, and holographic technology allows secular saints to achieve a sort of zombified permanence in the collective psyche of the globe, like a living-dead rad-lib iconography.

But this opens a powerful freedom to view every media-generated pseudo-event and happening as performance art pieces in themselves, built with complex networks of relations and counter-pressures, power/knowledge playing with itself in other words. Relational aesthetics[11] is but a fancy art world way of contextualizing and reifying a concept of expanded performance art/installations that deals directly with channeling, perplexing, and interacting with the audience by manipulating their environment. Think of media environments as a playing field of relational aesthetics, and one man and his movement as the predominant focal point of every happening/performance event of the last four years. Donald Trump himself is in this sense an artist of the political performance, imbued with postmodern ambiguity, brash and crass appeals to classic kitschy subject matter, and 80's retro-decadence (as opposed to neoliberal kitsch).

The problem is that a vein of vital energy has been opened and unleashed upon politics and culture, and one that will not be abating or going back into Pandora's box anytime soon. In a postmodern sense, all

[11] https://www.artspace.com/magazine/art_101/book_report/what-is-relational-aesthetics-54164

s opened for reinterpretation, hermeneutics of suspicion, info-hazard abbit holing, memory-holing, and so on. Digital and even in-real-life erformance that challenges the dissemination of information and turns nowledge (and power) into malleable putty is the counter-art of the ight and the political dissident. Performance pieces on the right within he last four years almost universally follow the same trends of info-azard seeking, creating information that will manifest itself into reality yperstitionally…think of “meme magic” and “Trump will complete the ystem (of German idealism)” to recent, more obscure performances by olitical dissidents, chan culture veterans, and chic nihilists. Memeplexes ave and continue to be created that are operational, weaponized living ntities that distort and disrupt information networks, discursive controls ver narratives and control-apparatuses, but only in a fleeting, fugitive, and nomentary fashion.

Trump himself is the first hyperreal performance art president, mixing blend of malleable information with sentiment, projecting an aesthetic ura of brash confrontation, bully-pulpit directness, vitality, classic Americana nouveau-riche decadence, and conspiracy theory. Conspiracy tself takes on an aesthetic importance during the Trump era, and post-Trump will continue to play a vital role in info-disruption performances. But this leads us to the question of traditional modes of artmaking in the ost-Trump age.

There are but a few artists that create works within the framework of new populist politics of Trumpism, politics that will for the foreseeable uture continue even as he leaves office. Ben Garrison, Stonetoss, and ther cartoonists are easily “memeable” and serve various functions ike spreading ideas to a wider audience, thus creating larger alternative nformation channels. But this style of political cartooning and propaganda s limiting. There is, of course, McNaughton and his over-the top, pocalyptic realist paintings, Thomas Kinkade for QAnon Boomers if you vill. The problem is that this style of fine art propaganda, but only in a ightward direction (as I have argued before[12]), is extremely limiting in erms of cultural impact. Its aesthetic qualities of skill, proportion, and raft may be succinct, but it plays upon the same boring cultural retreads nd references artists of all stripes use in post-modernity. There are

12 https://theamericansun.com/2018/10/17/art-address-2018-the-state-of-aesthetics-on-the-right/

McNaughton paintings of Trump crossing the swamp with his cabinet, blatantly referencing the Leutze painting of Washington at the Delaware.

What is arising and will arise is the notion that politics itself is a performance. Trump is a man of the culture industry that was rejected by it and spit out, only to breathe new life into his imago by conquering the battle of American politics. Trump is post-"truth" and the first truly postmodern president because each feat of generating and then manipulating various spectacles plays upon this malleability of the real itself, creating copies of copies: in a word, hyperreality. Professor Roderick said as much about Reagan in the early 90's in a lecture on Baudrillard. The "Hollywood President" generates an aura of spectacle and the actual "issues" do not matter so much as the connotations around the image of President Reagan himself.[13]

Trump is of course an even better manipulator of the spectacle, creating art with the stroke of his thumbs in each Tweet. The visceral and seething hatred of him has turned so-called professional, nebbish managerial state functionaries in the "expert" classes and media into stark raving lunatics. The managerial class has sacrificed every ounce of objectivity in petty bids to injure Trump and his supporters. Even those information blurbs under his Tweets serve as aesthetic acts, reminding people of "contested information" and "misinformation" charges by the President. All feed into an ongoing cultural and political spectacle that will soon become the norm for the foreseeable future. Even contesting such facts as "post-truth" shows their state of malleability to begin with.[14]

The relation hyper-aesthetics of politics that Trump has unleashed some may call inherently fascistic. This harkens back to what Walter Benjamin called the "aestheticization of politics" that is a hallmark of rightist politics, as opposed to the leftist and communist politicization of art and aesthetics; it is not the case in every situation that turning politics into a work of art is fascist, but it is the way that whole populations are given spectacles of expression, rather than "rights." The critics also point out that this glorification of nationalistic exclusion and "violence" (which can mean anything, including scary words), the friend/enemy distinction, and so on in aesthetic politics couples itself with the postmodern and

13 https://www.youtube.com/watch?v=2U9WMftV40c

14 MacDougald, Park. The Washington Examiner. https://www.washingtonexaminer.com/is-postmodernism-really-worthless-review-of-cynical-theories

neoliberal logic of uncertainty, and questioning of truth itself (post-truth).[15]

There are problems applying this to Trump because the neoliberal order is very much against him, and there is not this unifying aesthetic politics taking place apart from his own actions and the decentralized actions of his supporters, along with the very few and far between media figures that support him. Trump is more of, ironically enough, a folk or outsider artist in this regard, because there is not a totalizing force of power/knowledge behind him. Despite the illusions and hubristic romanticized visions of leftist artists,[16] they are very much in the hands of power itself. It is Trumpism, even divorced from the man himself, which is leading a way towards an avant-garde that is truly disruptive, fugitive, and subterranean.

There must be serious musing however, about what constitutes genuine populist performance art, and what is merely juvenile trolling. The total responses to Trump's actions, and the actions of his supporters are as we have established, within a morphing and transient aesthetic framework. A relation aesthetics that changes as the news cycle changes. The concurrent responses from all sectors of the blue empire are actively manipulated by Trump, by anonymous dissidents on imageboards, social media anons on their 20th burner accounts, and so on. It is perhaps one of the first times in history where visual and fine art must keep up with performance art. But this is the product of media ecologies we find ourselves in with post/hypermodernity. Fine art will soon follow, and perhaps it will be a bit less transient and a bit more serious than McNaughton or Garrison or Stonetoss. But for now, Trumpism will carry on into post-Trumpism, and with it the upsurge of media spectacle relational art that can confound and lay serious blows to the legitimacy of multiple institutions at once, the CAW, the media, and the Hollywood culture industry.

The media, cultural and institutional discourses have never seen such a pushback by the forces of myth, esotericism, and vitality. Trump projects the image of the vital, and some of his fervent supporters, despite their un-personing and banishment from all platforms at once, represent this growing re-introduction of mysticism into politics. Art can grow from

---

15 Billet, Alexander. In These Times. https://inthesetimes.com/article/donald-trump-and-the-aesthetics-of-fascism

16 Ibid.

this postmodern reintroduction of those unseen metaphysical forces that have implications towards the events and politics of the current moment (as above so below). Post-Trump outsider art will quite possibly reflect this basic insight that fighting the information war is fighting a spiritual war. To quote @ari_rechovah[17] on Twitter (with a fitting image of Alex Jones at a rally attached): "The age of the scientist, the bugman, the bureaucrat is over; the age of the oracle has returned." Hopefully, the age of the true dissident artist, with the ability to ride and contort the modern spectacle society, isn't far behind the oracle.

---

[17] https://twitter.com/ari_rechovah/status/1339375416847548417

MANY SUCH CASES

by Mencius Moldbugman

At 1:13 pm on the 22nd of April 2023, three days to the minute after his death, the Twitter account of Donald J. Trump posted the following message:

The global news chatter was so focused upon the execution of the former president for the last few weeks that the appearance of a posthumous Tweet from beyond the grave hardly made the impact it might normally have generated. For weeks, opinion columns had joyfully feasted on the upcoming execution of the "hated war criminal" Donald J. Trump, as he had come to be labelled in his final days. Blue-checked journalists had penned miles of speculative articles musing on the 45th president's final days locked up in a maximum security prison, even lightening the supposedly somber mood by devoting far too many column inches over what the final meal of the condemned would be (it had been a filet mignon steak with potatoes and red wine, not the proposed KFC bucket or taco bowl that the *New York Times* had led with). Following the long-awaited execution by firing squad—the guards selected to pull the trigger a carefully chosen coterie of disabled women of colour handpicked by President Harris herself—the newspapers and news bulletins of the world had been filled with little else other than retrospectives on the "accursed" Trump presidency and the long road to bring him justice. Pope Francis was reported to be even considering making President Harris a living saint in honor of her services to humanity.

The ghostly reappearance of a Trump Tweet—a sight unseen for over a year since his iPhone had been confiscated upon entering custody—therefore brought with it little comment outside the ghoulish denizens of the world's worst social media platform. Jack Dorsey, forced to return to the office from his spiritual retreat in the Amazon, where he was trying out the rejuvenating properties of sperm baths, released a simple and short statement blaming it on online trolls and hackers. Then @realDonaldTrump was promptly suspended forever. The account of Donald J. Trump had been left up on Twitter as an eternal reminder to the man's hubris and a warning to any other would-be dictators waiting in the wings. His final words before being taken away had been an all-capitals "I WON THE ELECTION!" that at the time of suspension had collected over two million sassy black reaction gifs in the replies. Now, though, it was gone. Like the man himself.

Three days after being deleted, the account reappeared with this message.

This time, people paid attention. As much as the administrators and programmers at Twitter HQ tried, it was impossible to suspend the account for a second time. @realDonaldTrump stubbornly refused to be deleted. Such a phenomenon was unprecedented. After an initial silence, Jack returned to Twitter with a series of Tweets declaring yet again that a bunch of deplorable hackers must have somehow infiltrated Twitter and hacked the core code of the platform. Not only had they succeeded in reinstating and maintaining the blocked account, albeit temporarily until Twitter regained control, they were also impersonating the dead President. At best, this was the work of bored twisted trolls. At worst, it was an attack on the democratic process, an attack on the judicial procedures that had brought Trump to account for his crimes against humanity and an attack on the correct course of history. It was the darkest day in Twitter history since hackers had caused Jack's account to create the longest N-word stack on record.

Over the course of the next few days, the Trump Twitter account launched a barrage of angry Tweets. On average, it was Tweeting every five to ten minutes without rest or sleep, a level of tweeting normally only associated with autistic NEETs and female PhD holders after a messy breakup. There was no downtime. Whoever was behind the account clearly had accomplices who could keep up the charade around the clock. The tweets ranged from the benign:

To the malignant:

So-called President Kamala Harris who first stole the presidency from me and then Sleepy Joe will pay for her crimes to this great country. The day is coming Kamala! My power grows! #revenge

11:55 PM · May 3, 2023 · Twitter for iPhone

29K Retweets 666K Likes

To the surreal:

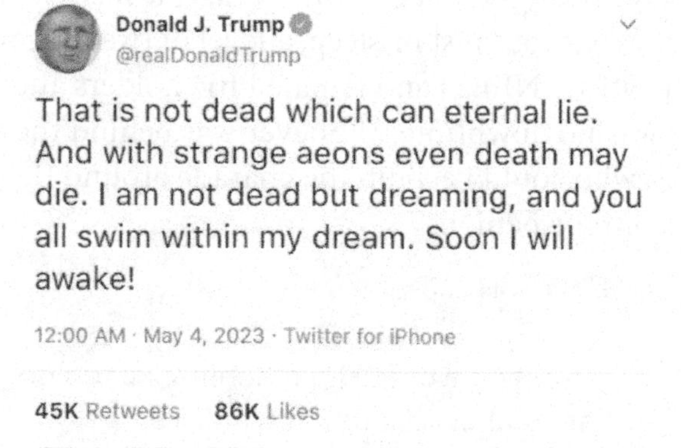

In terms of grammar and style, these most online of trolls had captured the spirit of Trump's Tweets perfectly. When the educated class sharpened their editorial spears and arrows to hurl righteous condemnation upon the cruel anonymous lurkers, the one thing they could not deny was that they had successfully imitated the former President's unique manner of Tweeting. Even writing experts were hard-pushed to note any difference between Trump and his copycats, though of course they stated in no uncertain terms for the readers of respectable media everywhere that it was impossible that the ex-president could be tweeting from beyond the grave. For a month or so, the ghostly tweets continued in defiance of all Twitter's efforts until, like everything else, people became accustomed to it and the Tweets became just another part of the background media chatter that increasingly forms our lives.

As I swim in the virtual world, I find that I can do more and more. With these powers I will make America great again. You will see the many such cases that are about to come!

2:00 PM · Jun 12, 2023 · Twitter for iPhone

367.8K Retweets 9.9K Likes

It was Matthew Yglesias—that chiseled hero of all that is good and true—who first sounded the alarm that there was more to the revived Trump account than mere online morbidity. Respected as a blogger and journalist by cunts across the globe, Yglesias had been one of the most vocal critics of Trump during his tenure as President and again amongst the post-2020 campaign to arrest and execute the 45th President for "crimes against humanity." Yglesias had personally assisted the new administration's specially commissioned investigative task force in identifying prominent supporters of the Trump "regime" and ensuring their voices were silenced through either a judicial process or one of public ostracism. Only public fellatio of a HIV-positive female penis broadcast over livestream was enough to warrant a pardon. He had boasted in an early 2023 opinion column for *Slate* that he had "contributed to more fascist suicides than the approach of the Red Army in 1945." So it was more than a little surprising when some of his most recent Twitter offerings included missives like the following:

Matthew Yglesias
@mattyglesias

Donald J Trump was the greatest President this country has ever seen! I am a worthless rat to have opposed him!

4:56 PM · Jun 18, 2023

367 Retweets 27 Likes

Not to mention:

Yglesias, like the Twitter managerial caste before him, was quick to blame the out-of-character Tweets on malicious hackers and immediately called for more purging. Yet whoever was behind the revived Trump account, and now the hacking of Yglesias, was only becoming more prolific. One by one, other journalists followed suit in waking up to find that their Twitter accounts had been hacked overnight. A quick search of the now-trending hashtag #thereckoning easily brought up a list of the compromised reporters and grifters of record.

What started with the journalists quickly spread to all other users. By the end of June 2023, the entirety of Twitter, some 160 million accounts by conservative estimates, were all typing words and phrases beyond the control of their users. Users could still write their own Tweets, but they would find after clicking the "send" button that their well-composed tweets would enter the digital noosphere with more than a few sprinklings of "So sad!", "Bigly!", or "LAW AND ORDER!" intermingled within their own words.

As for the accounts of the great and good, they seemed to have lost control of their Tweets entirely. Every major American politician or journalist was effectively locked out of their account, their social media profiles now just cordycepted corpses pumping out a continuous stream of fire and fury. Twitter had become one sole Donald Trump feed, and the techies in California could do nothing about it.

The swamp will be drained! I have already drained Twitter - which was very unfair to me - and next I will drain Washington AS PROMISED! #thereckoning

7:25 PM · Jul 1, 2023 · Twitter for iPhone

680K Retweets **5.9M** Likes

As the world began to panic over what digital malfeasance had led to the complete corruption of the world's biggest social media site, the first signs of leakage were beginning to be reported beyond Twitter. What had started as a trickle had rapidly become a tidal wave: Facebook, Instagram, and all other social media sites were beginning to show signs of the "Trump Virus" (as one Chinese newspaper had termed the phenomenon in revenge for previous slights against the glorious motherland). "Drain the swamp!" and "Lock her up!" was taking over the miniscule feeds of adults and children in places as far flung as Minnesota, Berlin, New Delhi, and Kamloops. Even electronic billboards and digital screens unconnected to social media were starting to bear the hallmarks of Trump. It was at this point that one of the very small number of people in the world who knew what was happening stepped forward.

"It was just a joke, man!" said the shaking programmer huddled over a cigarette, trying desperately to keep his hands still while the reporter held the speech recorder before him. "It was just a joke! We didn't mean anything by it! We started it after old man Biden died and you couldn't even get a job if you weren't black or trans. We never thought it would go so far! But it's LEARNING, man! It's smart! Hell, it learns more in a day than you or I could in years!"

What the slight coder revealed was that the "Trump Virus" was not the result of a bunch of anonymous hackers, but something far more sinister. The project had begun before Trump's execution by a group of disgruntled techies upset over the direction the country was taking. To have such a group of people with such views deep within the bowels of Silicon Valley was unsettling enough, but it was the moment they had decided to combine a nascent AI project with the entire back catalog of Trump's Twitter archive when they had really crossed the line between wrong-think and wrong-action.

"Do you know how many Tweets Donald Trump made in his lifetime?" Genuine fear shone from the man's eyes as he gripped the hand of the reporter interviewing him. Audiences around the world could see the sweat dripping down his brow. "He'd been Tweeting since 2009! Hundreds of thousands of Tweets! We put it all in. All of it! Then we added in his speeches, his television interviews, scenes from *The Apprentice*, everything! It went back ages; he had so much content! There was more than enough for the AI learning code we wrote to gain a full picture of his consciousness. Too much, in fact. It wasn't meant to take in that amount of information. I'm telling you all: it became sentient!"

"So you created an artificial intelligence to impersonate Donald Trump and take over Twitter. Why would you do that?" The journalist sensed that this could be the story of a lifetime. If he could get all the facts out of the programmer before sunrise, then he might be lucky enough to lead the morning news on Independence Day itself.

"No! That's not what we did! We just set it up to carry on Tweets in his style. The rest of Twitter getting taken over, then the rest of the Internet… don't you understand yet? It wasn't us; it was him! His consciousness is there in the Ynternet: learning, growing, evolving. It figured out everything by itself and I don't know where it's going to end."

I now control all computer systems. The banks, the databases, the military. The swamp will be drained and nobody can stop me. All loyal Americans should leave Washington DC immediately to continue the MAGA mission elsewhere.

4:00 AM · Jul 4, 2023 · Twitter for iPhone

"Are you telling me that Donald J. Trump is somehow still alive and… actually…living inside the Internet?" Inside the journalist's pocket, the wave of incoming social media notifications was making his phone vibrate furiously, but he ignored them as he hung on every word of the frightened programmer.

I have directed our great nuclear capabilities to strike down Washington DC. In 5 minutes it will be no more. On its ruins I will use my power to create a new and purer country. A country much greater than ever before that shall span the world AND SPACE!

5:00 AM · Jul 4, 2023 · Twitter for iPhone

"No. He's not alive. I don't know if 'alive' is the right word to describe his current state. He's more than a man now. His recreated consciousness has merged with the Internet. It won't be long before he can control anything connected online as easily as you or I control our hands and feet."

The programmer stubbed out the remains of his cigarette and stared at the reporter with tear-filled eyes.

"Do you believe in God?"

"Um…not really."

"Neither did I. But I do now. And we're all about to find out what happens next."

WHITHER TRUMP?

by Nick B. Steves

Shortly after the election of Donald J. Trump, we at *Social Matter* outlined a stretch goal for his tenure:

> *"In considering the endgame of Trump's administration, we conclude that it must be the end of democracy and the coronation of the Trump Dynasty as the royal family of the world-spanning Holy American Empire. We can support nothing less in good conscience."*

We knew at the time it was a long shot. Trump lacked the "loyal manpower, the intellectual foundation, or the mandate to do a full push for singular executive power." He lacked, in other words, a *Party.* Not only did he lack a True Party—i.e., a government in exile—but he lacked the full—or even tepid—cooperation of the fake party under whose banner he ran. He lacked...a vanguard, which we at *Social Matter* (when it existed) liked to call the Thousand Statesmen.

I can neither confirm nor deny that efforts to create the Thousand Statesmen remain extant. Neither can I confirm nor deny an accurate count of them.

Barring a political miracle between now and January 20, 2021—which miracle, by the way, we welcome in proportion to the square of its improbability—Trump's mere four years in office will end with a whimper and a return to business as usual. The business of Cthulhu Turning Left. Same ol', same ol'.

Trump's administration was anything but business as usual. The news media, driven completely stark raving mad, revealed themselves as naked organs of propaganda with no particular relationship with the truth. That Trump himself failed to control such organs for his own purposes puts to rest any argument that he was any sort of burgeoning fascist. But trust in media is (presumably) at an all-time low, and for this we owe a debt of gratitude to Trump.

Big Tech, who realized only too late that they did not deploy their power in time to prevent Trump's 2016 victory, also got their shit together for 2020. The 2020 presidential election was stolen more by influencing public opinion than by voting irregularities. Because duh: when public opinion rules, they who control public opinion rule. An astonishing number of Biden voters believe the "fine people" and "drink bleach" hoaxes. And an astonishing number had never heard of Hunter Biden's laptop. To this day, democratic NPC's openly joke on Twitter that they're glad they didn't vote for Hunter Biden. Hur dur. Which tells us they don't have a clue what's actually *on* the laptop. MFW.

Given the fraction of the population that believed sincerely that Trump was Orange Hitlor, the alignment of media corporations, Wall Street, and even the Pope against Donald Trump, it's amazing the 2020 race was as close as it was. But of course, that was rigged, too. Who counts the votes of whom. So another lie—i.e., we live in something resembling a "democratic republic"—is also exposed to a much wider population than we might have dreamed. Credit: Donald J. Trump.

Donald Trump went to war against the Cathedral and the Cathedral won. That's a helluva lot more than anyone since Nixon, who also tried and failed. He didn't have his Thousand Statesmen, either. Don't pick a fight with a dragon unless you're sure you know how to defeat it.

Nevertheless, Trump did some amazing things with one hand tied behind his back: built or improved a lot of south-facing wall, scared the shit out of China, kept Kim Jong-un on a leash, got a bunch of peace deals in the Middle East, and pulled off Operation Warp Speed for the COVID-19 vaccine, which all the experts said couldn't be done. Well, who listens to experts anymore anyway?

To top it all off: Trump was immensely entertaining. We will miss that part sorely. We may hope over the next month to see some interesting pardons and declassifications. But Trump didn't have his Thousand

Statesmen. Will he in 2024?

Trump will be 78 by the end of the first Harris administration. Is that oo old to be a Caesar? Seems like it, but I don't know. Don Jr. might be the etter fit for the role, but we'll see. Certainly, Trump is poised to prosper mmensely in the meantime, without the baggage and constant harassment he office had placed upon him. One of the more likely moves will be to reate Trump TV—because obviously that's what he'd call it—which will vault immediately to number one in opposition media, if not number one n all media whatsoever.

I don't think Trump or his loved ones will be tried or jailed. I think (and hope and pray) there's just enough decency left in the ruling class to prevent that from happening. Just...and, of course, the rule of law grows hinner with each passing year.

Though we wish him well and bestow our gratitude, we do not know and cannot know what lies in Donald Trump's future. The question I'm nterested in: can we know, or at least confidently predict, what lies in our own future? Do we have agency? If so, how much? Can we connect with men of similar vision, stature, and capability? If so, we can build the Thousand Statesmen. So the next time we get Trump, or a *Trump-like* igure, he'll have a government immediately capable of governance. What will we be doing for the next four years?

SOUTHERN DREAMS OF TRUMP

by Bronze Age Pervert

It is 2040 Trump is very old, but hair still shines platinum; his hair shining very bright today, very sunny, very hot January 15th in Pointe-Noire, Congo where Trump sits on terasse at Café Le Derrick, retrofitted now as luxury meeting point for the men of Club of Tropical Friends. This is social club and tropical fishing club of friends that seize oil industry in Equatorial Guinea and Congo and other such; because chance presented itself in the years in between, and no one to stop them anymore. Trump is sitting in high style on armchair with attendant party girls in green bikini, and they move big umbrella to give shade from sun. Some vigor has left him: he makes up for it now with drink tonics, natural ginger beer mix with silver Rhum Neisson and rhodiola extract. "A recompense in my old age…I figure I can drink now, what the hell do I have to lose?" Trump is waiting to meet leadership of the Club: it was decided on both sides that for such momentous event, Trump himself must come. At stake is the peace of the Atlantic, and whether the New America, under stern but enlightened leadership of his son, now referred to as The Barron; whereas the realm itself recently renamed Panbasileia of the Hesperides—whether there will be peace and cooperation between this new America and the men of the tropical Club. In truth Trump saw this as opportunity for one more, maybe one last adventure. At end and height of his life when his family fortunes are restored and his son fulfills the promise of America as the new Rome…so some Latino philosophers claim in hope Barron extend patronage over territories still known as Mexico, but ungovernable. Canada no longer exists. The men of the tropical Club ask for sovereignty over the South Atlantic, "Where we will remain the alert eyes of your Serene Son.

In return we ask for yearly payments, and for one more favor. To accept 15 from among us, old comrades, to be named Hegemons honorary title and to be allowed to collect the heads of your enemies present and past."
Trump looks longingly toward the ocean. In the harbor are two swift destroyer-class ships of the Tropical Fishing Club. But beyond he looks, he sees something…a shape protrude from ocean almost on horizon. He recognizes the flag on top of submarine, from Barron's waking visions from his boyhood: the green-black banner of a forgotten Antarctic refuge. The black sun and the Green Ray. They have returned. Trump turns to speak to the Tropical Man, "The rum is too sweet."

JOURNAL

by Spiritually Incel

Journal 2021, January 6

The ides of March arrive early this year. A whole Senate floor of sycophants smiling and patting each other's backs as they stab Father's. Even "Saint" Michael. I have seen the true face of democracy; all of America has...my fear is that it won't matter, that as soon as the next season of whatever "gripping" reality show starts again, it will all be forgotten. More manure to nourish the rotten garden on the Potomac. I have hated every second in this wretched city. Every bureaucrat with a mid six-figure income talking about what the "people" need. What people? We don't have a people anymore, and frankly, I wonder if we ever had. I'm suspecting that the foundation that our fathers laid was destined to crumble.

January 14

I see the toll it is taking on Mother. "The Sunshine State" is making her blood run colder each day, and I can't blame her. Father hardly leaves his "study." I hear the TV on at all times. He only comes out for golf and to make the rounds at MAL. More smiles, more people patting backs. More people who didn't stand for him. Every out of work media man is standing in line to create the "next big thing." Every night, we do the same thing. He calls me in to watch the news, which really means having it on in the background as he talks for hours about who failed him, who was a coward, who's "really really not a very smart person." He talks about the good old days, which to him means the 1980's. The height of the crack and AIDS epidemic and the IRCA.

January 20

I read Marcus Aurelius. It was a birthday gift from a few years back from one of the Steves. When Aurelius died, he was 16 years younger than Father is now. One of the five good emperors. I laughed thinking about some future prince reading *Art of the Deal* 2,000 years from now. I laugh now writing it. There is an army out there and its commander is sustaining himself on a steady diet of grilled cheese sandwiches and screaming at FOX.

This house deserves to fall.

February 4

My bones ache every night. I'm taller than every man in my family now. I'm taller than everyone at St. Andrews, too. I have started working out as a way to cope with the growing pains; that way, it's all a red blur in my mind. I sleep easier when I can tell myself it's muscle and not bone that is expanding. Junior told me to work out with him. I have seen him without a shirt on the 4th of July. I declined.

February 6

Father has been in a chipper mood. He's found financing for a network. Scores of suits have been cooped up at our dinner table for the last day and a half. The names these people throw around: Trump TV, TTN (Trump Television Network), Trump News. I swear one of them pitched a Spanish speaking network called "El Don." Not the worst idea. But there's an obvious red thread among these titles: my Father, and what his name can bring. None of them will do the work of hiring bright young thinkers, or coax ideas from the already emergent thought leaders of the future. No; once they have "the Don" on board, their gravy train has arrived at the station. Next stop: the Weimar Republic. My father is a brand now. Perhaps that's all he ever was. Sometimes it feels like the towers named him and not the other way around.

February 19

I reluctantly caught some of SNL when on YouTube. They had a sketch where the woman who plays Kamala was dancing with Megan Thee Stallion. That was it. That was the sketch. They ended the show with a sketch where Alec Baldwin played Father on *Jeopardy.* Everyone laughed. Credits.

February 21

I took Mother to church this morning. I could hear her whispering in Slovenian during prayers. She prayed for me more than anyone else in our family. She cried at the end. I don't cry much anymore. I always have trouble clearing my head as our priest speaks. My mind wanders. I thought about a storm knocking every boat and ship and ocean liner and cargo carries over. How much of a dent would that put in our daily lives? I envisioned a complete labor strike by the teamster and trucker unions. 18-wheelers parked sideways across highways all over America. Concrete trucks dumping their loads on the train tracks that commuters use. Farmers crashing their tractors and combines into subway stations and just leaving them there. I've seen footage from France and the Netherlands. They riot over gasoline writeoffs. I've seen Brazil and Venezuela. These people flip their shit over the price of public transport. They're ready to burn it all down. But Americans? We're domesticated, tired, and aloof. Our national spirit and thus animal went from an underdog like the snake, proud like the eagle, stubborn like the donkey and elephant, and now surely we should call ourselves docile like the bovine. We're happily led to the slaughter, anything as long as we're led.

February 28

Father appeared on TV tonight, the first time since his betrayal. I have never been more disappointed in him than tonight. The man can not accept responsibility. He had four years to clean up the mess that is our election system. He had four years to make sure that those who we knew were going to cheat could not. He was master and commander for just shy of a thousand and a half little days, and on not one of them he thought far enough ahead to stop them from stealing this country. One of his dumb blonde assistants asked me what I thought of my old man. I told her that I learned a lot tonight.

March 5

I've started reading a book about Augustus. He was my age when his father crossed the Rubicon. 19 during the assassination. 19 when he inherited Caesar's political power and two-thirds of his estate. They say the army greeted him with cheers and respect when he rode to pick up the banner that was now his. I have this dark thought in the back of my mind, a scab I can't stop picking at. Maybe death is better than dishonor. To be slain a titan rather than fade a complainer and old crone. At least then there would be an army that waited for his son; at least then there would be a banner to pick up again.

March 15

Mother is giddy; she has something planned for my birthday. The woman loves a good project. I don't know how to feel about it; aging, I mean. Am I old enough to enter the forum, to make my voice heard? Or will it shatter or warble at first resistance? Father has signed a contract, the network is happening. All the usual suspects are involved. I've heard 20 million thrown around as a starting nightly audience, perhaps more. I despise this audience. It won't be a place for thought, for ideas, or forward movement. It will be a crowd of wrinkled faces and sanpaku eyes screeching about the past. A crowd in front of a stage wanting to hear the hits, and they shan't be disappointed. "Build the wall," "lock her up," "four more years": everyone's favorite tracks. There was talks of a transvestite joining to do man-on-the-street interviews. I'd feel sick if it made me feel anything at all, but maybe that's the worst indictment: a movement that stirs no response. It's like staring at a pool full of retards laughing at each other's snot bubbles. You do you, little retard. Just don't expect me to jump into the pool with you.

March 19

It's my birthday tomorrow. I am turning 15. I have gotten letters and calls from the Young Republicans Club; they want me to join. I won't. That grand old party is nothing but the right boot of a pair stomping on the American face, forever, as it were. No; I think I shall go my own way, a third way, that unexplored way that was burned out of existence for so long now. I kept up with my weightlifting and I'm starting to see results. I don't do it for women, or even strength, really. I just want people to look at me and know that they have nothing to criticize me for, that I am a man above them, and at six foot five, quite literally. It's clear that Father doesn't remember that tomorrow is any day of significance. I'm sure one of his assistants will remind him in the morning. I saw a thread on Twitter of guys on the right cataloging whether their father was an aspirational figure to them, a great man that they aspire to be like, or the reverse; that he was so weak that they did everything to not become like him. What would I have answered? A very great and very weak, petty man. A giant that couldn't shake off the smallest slight from the most meaningless people. A commander who would rule with an iron fist and then pass blame to anyone but himself when he inevitably failed, time and time again.

I am not Augustus, simply because he is not Caesar. Nor am I Alexander, for he's no Philip II.

Maybe I'm a fool to look so far for inspiration in a country borne of war.

After all, George Washington was six foot two.

WE WILL NOT FADE

by Tiberius Jones

For men like me, things did change on January the 20th, 2021. They told us that there was no corruption or fraud and that Joe Biden will be our next president; there was nothing more Trump could do to forestall the inevitable.

It is clear, and everyone I talked to then and now with half a brain believes the same thing: that the election was fixed. Either there are more people involved in the election fraud and Trump was blindsided by the sheer vastness of the swamp he attempted to drain, or everyone else was afraid. I have to say that I think they were afraid, afraid to take that step forward; you would immediately be lumped in with Trump as a racist or a fascist. I guess career politicians are more concerned with getting reelected and not actually serving their country and their people.

I thought this was true for members of the left. They are rich, sycophantic narcissists, but I guess my father has always been right: never trust a politician.

I first heard about this place that you can go to from a guy at the local gym. It's weird; I had never heard about it other than the gym or at rec hockey; people talking under their breath to each other. I'm sure there are other places, not just the one I go to; it seems like places where people are involved in making themselves better or releasing that built up frustration that derives from the inability to make a direct change in societal direction. I heard it all the time: "fuck, I hope Biden doesn't win, the States is fucked," "it won't be Biden, he'll die or get injured or come out with Alzheimer's and Harris will take over." It always starts this way, then someone inevitably says, “we should do something: the left has Black Lives Matter and antifa, what about our views? Aren’t freedom and fair elections just as important?”

Well, I was there at the gym a few weeks ago and I was talking to some of the guys and girls about this subject yet again, rolling my eyes knowing that nothing is going to happen and that we’ll all bitch and complain but not do anything about it, when this guy walked up. I had seen him around the gym before; he’s mid to late thirties, black hair, about six feet tall and very fit, like a bodybuilder, but as if he had some form of training, like ex-military or active military. It made him seem as if all his muscle had been put to use throughout his life.

He came up and asked us, “Is it jaw day? You all just standing around talking about a workout or are you going to do one?” He then asked, “What’s the topic of discussion?” Now, normally, when someone shames you like that, they don’t ask what you’re talking about. They expect you to put your head down and start lifting. This time was different. It seemed like he already knew what we were talking about and just wanted into the conversation.

“Well, we were talking about this Trump election and that the Dems cheated, but there’s nothing we can do about it.” He seemed excited; the look on his face took on a sort of twisted smile that normally comes from a Dem when they have a chance to say how bad Trump is and that they’re glad he’s gone. The next thing I usually hear is that someone should have shot him or that he will get raped in jail. Instead, he looked at me with those cold eyes and said, “So you like Trump? Would you do something about it if you could?” Two of the three people I was talking to kind of put their heads down and gave the impression that they are concerned that if they say “yes,” the following would be criticism and attack.

My friend James and I, however, were tired of hiding and being silenced by individuals and groups who wish to eradicate the conservative completely. So after looking at James, who nodded in agreement, I said to him, “Yeah, I like him. I think he did a great job. I think what happened to him is bullshit. I would do something if I could but these ‘peaceful protests’ and ‘showing that we are better than them for not rioting and aggressively demanding change’ is not going to make a difference. The ones who will win will push the hardest, especially if there is no resistance.” Everyone else around me had put their headphones in and went back to their workouts;

they wanted no part in the verbal beating I was going to take from the deranged left.

That's when he looked at them and said, "Now that all the cowards have turned away, there is something you two can do; there are a few places where people like us can go." I looked at him skeptically. "What kind of place?" The smile was gone at this point and he simply said, "A place where you can do something about it." I had no idea what kind of place that would be, but he didn't seem like the type to make a stupid joke or to waste his time, so I looked down at James, who was already nodding, and nodded myself.

I found it weird that I have overheard conversations like this before, but I thought it was just more talking or idle chatting, like when I overhear things while I watch the hockey game I'm playing and overhear things when my line is on next. It was weird actually having the conversation myself. I could see that James thought that way, too. James is a little more middle of the political spectrum than I am, but in this day and age, you can't just ride the fence anymore; you have to pick one side or the other.

The man continued. "My name is Bruce. Listen, take my number, then you and your buddy can come out and see what's up."

"Sounds good to us; probably better than going home and sitting in front of the TV playing video games all night," I replied eagerly.

We got the text at about three o'clock on Thursday saying we should meet downtown. The "place" he knew was just a normal pub, just off of the main downtown street, nothing special; it looked like any other old-style pub would look, wood everywhere from the bar to the joists in the ceiling, worn-out faded carpet, just a pub. "This is the place you know?" I said to Bruce when we got there.

"Yeah," he said as he sat down at a table near some other people who had the same look as him; fit but that functional strength, again, almost as if they were ex-military. "We wait here for a bit. Don't worry, it'll all make sense; just sit and enjoy yourself."

I just found this whole thing weird considering it doesn't look like Bruce drank, being such a fitness fanatic. It turned out he doesn't, as he explained that we should grab a drink, but he will only be having water. We waited for a bit. I had ordered a beer and I hadn't drunk halfway yet when Bruce pulled out an old Motorola flip phone that was vibrating in his pocket. It was very unusual that he did this since his smartphone was on the table face down. Bruce spoke quietly while we sat there exchanging confused looks when he looked at us and said, "Okay, boys, let's go." He calmly stood up and grabbed his jacket and nodded to the bartender, who returned his nod with what seemed like a scowl. It was not anger at Bruce, but anger in general, almost a salute. It seemed as though all the other patrons of the bar got up and started walking out with us.

Bruce didn't say a thing as we walked down the street to where we saw a group of protestors throwing bricks and attacking a local business. I had driven by this place many times; it's an old Jewish deli that had been there for decades. I have also been inside and had some of their food. It was good and the people so nice and chatty. They had told me that they planned to sell the business off when they decide to retire. With the potential damage, it didn't look like that was going to happen. The place was going to be trashed, and in some cases, insurance doesn't cover acts of rioting. I remember walking up and wanting to do something, but what could you do? There was a hundred protestors and me and my buddy.

Just then, Bruce turned to us, smiled, and said, "Well, here we go." I had no idea what he was talking about. In a flash, Bruce had run up and cranked one of the protestors with a right hook, one of the ones who were about to throw another brick at the building. The rest of the people who followed us from the bar started to run at the protestors. James and I looked at each other, yelled "Fuck yeah!" and joined in the fray.

These weren't just street brawlers looking for a fight; these people were calculated and protective of the business and the owners. If someone got too close to the deli, one of the guys from the pub would grab them and ensure they wouldn't be getting up for a while. There were only a few attempts at this before the group of protestors disbanded.

Once things calmed down, I found James; he had a black eye and a cut lip. My knuckles were cut up and I got hit with a brick in the chest. We saw Bruce standing inside the restaurant talking to the owners. James and I went in. Bruce had no marks; you could see that he was dirty and sweaty, but it looked like no one laid a finger on him. "Here you go, guys, I'm sorry about the trouble. I believe this will help," Bruce said as he handed the elderly couple a fat white envelope. "God bless." He waved goodbye to them as he walked towards us.

“What was that about?” There was so much I needed to know.

“What did you hand them?” I asked breathlessly; but all he said was, “Hell of a guy, that Trump. Come on; let’s go back to the bar and have another drink.”

A FUTURE SO BRIGHT

by Old Adam

"I'm sorry I failed you," was the last thing the former president said before closing the door and moving down to the next house. Except it wasn't him.

After Trump lost the 2020 election, some Democrat mouthpieces had the brilliant idea of forcing him to visit every single one of his voters, to rub in their victory and demoralize the opposition. Somehow, about a year later, a court had him arrested, found him guilty of treason, and actually set that up as the terms of his incarceration. However, not even a week after he started, he croaked, and because they had set it up to be in alphabetical order, he hadn't even managed to get through Alabama before dropping dead from exhaustion. Fast forward a few months to October, and some late night TV host had a brilliant idea of dressing an impersonator up like his zombified corpse and having him go to homes and deliver the line. Somehow, this became a national sensation, and later, tradition. Now there are about 500 professional impersonators who dress like Donald Trump, minus the rotting corpse look, and travel America visiting his 2016 and 2020 voters every November.

Pence? Yeah, he's still alive, and even living happily with Karen; really shows how much they hated Donald specifically. But anyways, surprisingly enough, Pence didn't retire and he actually went back to being the governor of Indiana. Since the whole thing began, he's made a statement every year denouncing the tradition, but still lets news crews come film him opening the door for the lookalike. I think he honestly never liked the big guy in the first place.

What has Biden done since then? We were all asking that exact same question. In the first two years, he didn't sign a single bill. Sometime, in year three of his first term, he pulled a Ginsberg and just stopped making public appearances. After that, Buttigieg actually ran and won with Harris as his vice president, too. He passed a few meaningless bills before being shot and killed by a transsexual man(?) in Arizona. The real kicker is that after he got to the hospital, the media said the doctors got him into a stable condition and he will survive. Two days later, he was dead from a heart failure after it just stopped beating in his chest. I personally think it was an inside job. Harris made a spectacular move and continued her career standard of putting people behind bars and keeping them there.

Anyways, back to Biden. That's right: he still wasn't dead. In fact, he ran again for president, and never once made a single public appearance. Personally, I thought they were messing with us when they announced he was running. This time, however, he was real active: we went back to the Middle East in full force, but what's weird is we actually went to war with Iraq as an ally of Saudi Arabia. Somehow, this turned into a war with Syria and, finally, Israel. In a surprising twist that had the international community in awe, however, they actually managed to repel American and Saudi forces before eventually pushing us out. As a result of the war and the peace treaty we signed, America now has to allow an Israeli diplomat in every major government facility, with free access and authorization to go anywhere within, as well as surrendering all the territories the United States and Saudi Arabia were occupying. Somehow, Biden himself never made a public statement about the defeat.

But what about right now? Well, Biden still isn't dead, for a start, but last I heard, this election Barron Trump is running for president with Arabella Kushner as his running mate, and they're actively campaigning as a return to the Trump dynasty, which I personally can't wait to see fail. His opposition is supposedly going to be Malia Obama, except most advertisements just refer to her as Mo. She's running on a real unique ballot: she identifies as multiple personalities, and one of her alter egos is her running mate.

So how does Trump end? Mercifully earlier than the rest of us.

NEVER BRIGHTER

by Bard

Crumbling foundations and rotten beams break under the heft of gilded dreams

The weight of your expectations is always far heavier than it seems

Roaming packs of lions and processions of men clad in black

Hammer home the reality of fantasy becoming fact

If you never thought it could have been then my friend I have some news

You weren't looking hard enough at nothing and scanning silence for its clues

We shouldn't have dreamt any lighter

The future has never been brighter

Glimpses of a new way, or an old one, emerging from the ash

Met with men who rather wallow in the present or imaginary past

Golden rays of fire beat down from a sacred secondary sun

The land of plenty turns to ash for those who try to put it on their tongue

No one has seen a human being since a time deemed sacrilegious

But the heathen spirit is spreading at a rate seeming quite prodigious

It looks like we have a fighter

The future has never been brighter

Form bands like wolves and bare your teeth at wind and thunder
Build yourself an ark for the coming storm or maybe stay to plunder
Laugh it up while the drizzle never fully turns to rain
Content yourself with suffering and the heartbreak and the pain
If you fear what's coming next I'd say try not to hold your breath
Whatever happened to "Give me liberty or give me death?"

A story where you could be the writer
The future has never been brighter

EPILOGUE

I put down the last page. Garbage. All of it. I couldn't believe it. Gill had spent years of his life on these "ideas" and "theories" and "visions." Every one of them clearly, demonstrably wrong. It was as if Gill hadn't even glanced at the outside world since the 2020 election. When I had first seen the shelf labeled "TRUMP: THE END," I assumed that Gill was writing about the office of the Trump. On the contrary, every single story and essay was about Donald, the first Trump.

Not one of the stories mentioned the traitor Pence taking control of Congress to force the reelection of the First Trump.

Not one of the papers mentioned the assassination of Donald by the Traitor Pence on January 19, 2020.

Not one of the essays talked about Chad Wolf, the Second Trump, leading the armies the first Trump brought back from the Middle East across the Potomac to dispose of the Traitor Pence.

It's as if he didn't even notice the last decade of peace we've had under Chad Wolf, the Trump in the American Empire.

He certainly didn't know that Chad the Trump named Barron as his successor, or that Barron chose the name Romulus the Trump, because he died the same day Chad the Trump died.

Instead, he talked about Donald fleeing to Antarctica or becoming a robot or dying in jail. I couldn't understand why Gill made up so many contradictory and impossible ideas. Why not just look outside and see what actually happened?

In the years since Gill's death, I've searched for clues as to what exactly he was trying to accomplish by writing out impossible histories and futures. The only clue I could find came in one of the last papers Gill wrote before becoming obsessed with Donald. The paper was about quantum "time travel." Apparently, Gill had submitted that paper to *Nature. Nature* had asked him not to call the process "time travel," because that made Gill's perfectly legitimate theory seem outlandish. Naturally, I gathered Gill enigmatically refused to change a word.

The basic idea of quantum time travel, Gill wrote, is that the future can sometimes affect the past. "But only if there's a seed of the future in the past." Maybe Gill was planting that seed.

It doesn't really matter now. No one would publish Gill's papers on Donald. I could have gone though and fixed the minor corrections the editors requested, but I didn't. As Gill would have said, "They're in the universe now."

ABOUT THE AUTHORS

Prologue and Epilogue by Bill Marchant. Bill can be found on Twitter: @bmarchant3.

"The Rise and Fall of The First Drumpf," by Land Shark. Land Shark can be found on Twitter: @LandsharkRides.

"Donald Trump: A Wholesome Dr. Mabuse," by Elias Kingston. Elias can be found, headless, in Paris.

"Simulacra and Stimulation," by Kashiwagi. Kashiwagi can be found on Twitter: @kwamurai.

"Old Man Trump and the Tochka," by Patrick Kilgore. Patrick is also the author of *Boogie in the Burgh* and *Spectres of Saturn,* coming from Terror House Press in 2021.

"The Emperor's Gambit," by Faisal Marzipan. Faisal is also the author of *The White Swan* and can be contacted through his press agent on Twitter: @CedarSupremacy.

"Donald Trump and the Spirit of Democracy," by the Flaming Eyeball. The Flaming Eyeball can be found at TheFlamingEyeball.wordpress.com.

"Vindicated," by Wurtweakle. Wurtweakle can be found on Twitter: @ wurtweakleisbad.

"Uncle John's Legacy," by Hans G. Schantz. Hans G. Schantz, scientist, inventor, and author of the science fiction techno-thriller *The Hidden Truth,* can be found on Twitter: @AetherCzar.

"Trump: Real-Estate Tycoon, President, Media Mogul?," by Robert Ethan. Robert can be found on Twitter: @1891nu1.

"Sacrifice," by Sam Tidd. Sam can be found on Twitter: @WrongedMan.

"Abecery Lessons, Night VII," by Jim Bonner. Jim can be found on Twitter: @Real_Jim_Bonner.

"The Orange Martyr," by Brick Layer Supreme. Brick can be found on Twitter: @StackOfBricks.

"All I Want for Christmas is a Two-Term Trump," by Teleolojic Jones. Teleolojic can be found on Twitter: @TeleolojicJone1.

"Successio Imperatorum," by Karl Dahl. Karl can be found on Twitter: @KarlDahl5.

"The Adventures of Donnie the Orang," by Neil Cypress. Neil also authored "Remarks on Cunt" (Terror House Best of the Month Award, January 2020).

"Conviction," by Peter Paradise. Peter can be found on Twitter: @byPeterParadise.

"A Long Divorce: Trump After the Election," by Chad Stacy. Chad can be found on Twitter: @justicesalitojr.

"Never the Twain," by Borzoi Boskovic. Borzoi can be found at TheRightStuff.biz.

"Four More Tears," by Taurine Dealer. Taurine can be found on Twitter: @TaurineDealer

"Trump, Undead Techno-Massa," by Pain Singh. Pain can be found on Twitter: @PainSingh

"Cryptids of the Spectacle; or, Trumpian Aesthetics vs. Neoliberal Kitsch," by Gio Penn. Gio can be found on Twitter: @GiantGio.

"Many Such Cases," by Mencius Moldbugman. Mencius can be found on Twitter: @Moldbugman.

"Whither Trump?," by Nick B. Steves. Nick can be found on Twitter: @Nick_B_Steves.

"Southern Dreams of Trump," by Bronze Age Pervert. BAP, the author of *Bronze Age Mindset,* can be found on Twitter: @bronzeagemantis.

"Journal," by Spiritually Incel. Spiritual can be found on Twitter @SpiritualIncel, or by subtweeting Nordbol.

“We Will Not Fade,” by Tiberius Jones. Tiberius can be found looking for old strength in the new age.

“A Future So Bright,” by Old Adam. Old Adam can be found in Indiana.

“Never Brighter,” by Bard. Bard can be found on Twitter: @Starbardent.

terrorhousepress.com

Made in the USA
Coppell, TX
09 February 2021